Essential Maths Skills for
A-Level Physics

Love it or loathe it, maths is a big deal in the new Physics AS and A-Levels
— without it, you could lose out on 40% of the overall marks. Ouch.

Not to worry. This brilliant CGP book explains all the maths you're likely to meet
during the course, with plenty of step-by-step examples to show you how it works.

We've also included practice questions (with answers) to make sure you've got to grips
with everything. Those maths marks are looking a lot more achievable all of a sudden...

A-Level revision? It has to be CGP!

Published by CGP

Editors:
Emily Garrett, Rachael Marshall, Sam Pilgrim, Charlotte Whiteley, Sarah Williams

ISBN: 978 1 78294 471 3

With thanks to Mark Edwards for the proofreading.
With thanks to Jan Greenway for the copyright research.

Clipart from Corel®
Printed by Elanders Ltd, Newcastle upon Tyne.

Based on the classic CGP style created by Richard Parsons.

Contents

Words that are highlighted in **orange** are defined in the Glossary.

Significant Figures

Significant figures might not be the most exciting topic to start a book with, but you'll need to think about them in pretty much every calculation you do in physics, so it's a good idea to get the hang of them early on.

Almost **All Values** are Given to a Number of **Significant Figures**

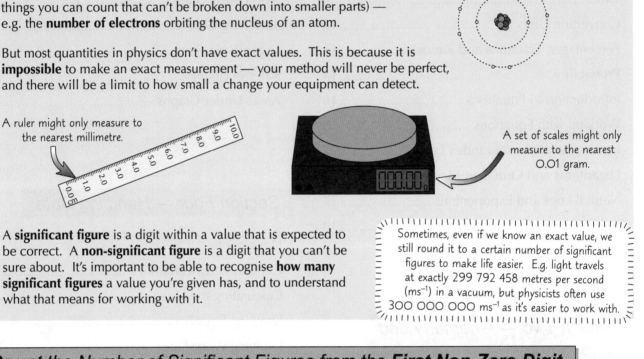

Occasionally in physics you might come across an **exact value** (often for things you can count that can't be broken down into smaller parts) — e.g. the **number of electrons** orbiting the nucleus of an atom.

But most quantities in physics don't have exact values. This is because it is **impossible** to make an exact measurement — your method will never be perfect, and there will be a limit to how small a change your equipment can detect.

A ruler might only measure to the nearest millimetre.

A set of scales might only measure to the nearest 0.01 gram.

A **significant figure** is a digit within a value that is expected to be correct. A **non-significant figure** is a digit that you can't be sure about. It's important to be able to recognise **how many significant figures** a value you're given has, and to understand what that means for working with it.

> Sometimes, even if we know an exact value, we still round it to a certain number of significant figures to make life easier. E.g. light travels at exactly 299 792 458 metres per second (ms^{-1}) in a vacuum, but physicists often use 300 000 000 ms^{-1} as it's easier to work with.

Count the Number of Significant Figures from the **First Non-Zero Digit**

To find the number of significant figures a value is given to:

1) **Start** counting at the **first non-zero digit**.
2) **Stop** counting at the **last non-zero digit**, or the last digit after the **decimal point** (if there are any).

So: **385.67 s** is given to **5** significant figures
      1 2 3 4 5

5.006 W is given to **4** significant figures
    1 2 3 4

605 000 g is given to **3** significant figures
    1 2 3

100 001 km is given to **6** significant figures
     1 2 3 4 5 6

> You can use significant figures to estimate the uncertainty of a value (p.72).

Zeros at the **End** of a Number are **Significant** if They Come **After** a **Decimal Point**

This is because zeros after a decimal point give you **extra information**:

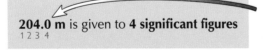

204.0 m is given to **4 significant figures**
1 2 3 4

You might not think that you need this final zero — using 204 m would give you the same answer in any calculation. But this zero is **significant** — if it wasn't included, you wouldn't know if this length was exactly 204 m, or if it was rounded down from 204.1 m.

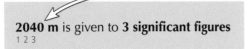

2040 m is given to **3 significant figures**
1 2 3

On the other hand, this final zero **doesn't** tell you anything about how many significant figures the measurement has. You **can't tell** if the distance was measured as 2040 m to **4 significant figures**, or whether it was measured as e.g. 2043 m, and **rounded** down to 2040 m to **3 significant figures**. You **always assume** the smallest **number** of significant figures, so you'd say this number was given to **3 significant figures**.

Significant Figures

Zeros at the Start of a Number are Not Significant

Look back at the rule on page 2 — you don't start counting until the first **non-zero** digit.

So: **0.045 m** is given to **2** significant figures.   **0.000403 g** is given to **3** significant figures.

> This makes sense if you think about converting the same number into **different units** (p.8) — 0.045 m is the same as 4.5 cm or 0.000045 km — these are all **different ways** of writing the **same information**, so they must all have the same number of **significant figures**.

There's an Important Rule for Significant Figures in Calculations

As a rule of thumb:

> You should round your final answer to a calculation to the **same number of significant figures** as the data value with the **fewest** significant figures used in the calculation.

You can give your answer to 1 more significant figure than the data value with the fewest significant figures in the calculation if you're doing the OCR A or OCR B course.

The exception to this is when you're working with **logarithms** and **exponentials** — they have their own rules, which are coming up on p.25.

When rounding your answer, look at the digit to the right of the last significant figure you'll be including — if it's less than 5 round down, if it's 5 or more round up.

> It's a good idea to write down the **unrounded answer** as part of your working, then give the **rounded answer** along with the **number of significant figures** you're giving it to.

If you use your answer in another calculation, use the unrounded answer.

Worked Example

The potential difference across a component in a circuit is 5.0 V and the current through it is 3.25 A.
Using the equation resistance = potential difference ÷ current, calculate the component's resistance.

1 Do the calculation. $5.0 \div 3.25 = 1.538461...$ *Don't round your answer yet.*

2 Look at the significant figures in the question.
The p.d. is 5.0 V, so it's given to 2 significant figures, and the current is 3.25 A, so it's given to 3 significant figures.

3 Round your answer.
Potential difference has the fewest significant figures (2) so the final answer should also be given to 2 significant figures.

3 is less than 5, so round down.
$1.538461... = 1.5 \, \Omega$ (to 2 s.f.)
State how many s.f. your answer is given to.

Practice Questions

Q1 How many significant figures are each of these values given to?
   a) 154 654 Ω b) 14 010 m   c) 24.300 V   d) 0.000450 A

Q2 What is 1572.86 °C to: a) two significant figures?   b) three significant figures?   c) four significant figures?

Q3 A car travels 522 m in 37 seconds. Calculate the car's average speed, giving your answer to an appropriate number of significant figures (*speed = distance ÷ time*).

I wish my bank balance was a bit more of a significant figure...

The rule about significant figures in calculations is a really important one. It's also going to be used on almost every page of this book, so it's a good idea to get familiar with it. At least it's pretty simple though.

Standard Form

A lot of numbers that come up in physics are written in standard form.

Standard Form Gets **Rid** of Some **0s**

Standard form **tidies up** very big or very small numbers in calculations.

For example:

There are about 31 600 000 seconds in a year. In standard form, this is:

$$3.16 \times 10^7 \text{ s}$$

This means $3.16 \times 10 \times 10 \times 10 \times 10 \times 10 \times 10 \times 10$.

In standard form, this number is always between 1 and 10.

The size of the charge on an electron is about 0.000 000 000 000 000 000 160 C.

In standard form, you'd write:

$$1.60 \times 10^{-19} \text{ C}$$

This −19 means that you divide 1.60 by ten, nineteen times (see p.23 for more about indices).

We call numbers that haven't been written in standard form 'decimal form'.

Numbers in Standard Form Are Written in a **Particular Way**

Numbers in standard form will always look like this:

This number is always between **1** and **10**.

$$A \times 10^n$$

This is the **how many places** the **decimal point** would have to move if you wrote the number out in full.

To convert a number from **decimal form** into **standard form**:

- Put the decimal point after the **first non-zero value** in your number, followed by any other significant figures. This is **A**.
- **Count** how many places the **decimal point** has moved. This is **n**. *n* is **negative** if the decimal point has moved to the **right**, and **positive** if the decimal point has moved to the **left** (so *n* is negative for numbers that are between −1 and 1).

$A = 2.59$

$$25\ 900 \text{ m} = 2.59 \times 10^4 \text{ m}$$

The decimal point moves four places to the left, so $n = 4$.

To convert a number from **standard form** into **decimal form**:

- Move the decimal point **n places**. It moves to the **left** if *n* is **negative**, and the **right** if *n* is **positive** (the opposite way around from above).

$n = -3$, so move the decimal point 3 places to the left.

$$3.2 \times 10^{-3} \text{ Hz} = 0.0032 \text{ Hz}$$

$A = 3.2$

Be careful with **significant figures** and zeros after decimal points (p.2-3) when you're working in standard form:

1) If you know $c = \textbf{300 000 000 ms}^{-1}$ **(to 3 s.f.)**, and you wanted to write *c* in **standard from**, you'd write $c = \textbf{3.00} \times \textbf{10}^8 \textbf{ ms}^{-1}$ **(to 3 s.f.)** — make sure you include digits for all the significant figures.

2) If you knew a star was $\textbf{4.0} \times \textbf{10}^{13}$ **km (to 2 s.f.)** away, and you wanted to write this in **decimal form**, you'd write **40 000 000 000 000 km (to 2 s.f.)** — if the '(to 2 s.f.)' wasn't included, someone might think it was just to 1 s.f.

Use a **Calculator** When you Work With Values in Standard Form

To enter a value in standard form into your calculator, type in the normal part (*A* in the box above), then press either: ×10ˣ or EXP or EE depending on your calculator. Then type in the power (*n*).

Your calculator might display a number in standard form like this: `9.58    04`

This is the same as $\textbf{9.58} \times \textbf{10}^4$.

Standard Form

Worked Example

The Earth moves around the Sun in a roughly circular orbit at a distance of 150 000 000 000 m. It takes one year to complete one orbit.

a) **Calculate how far the Earth travels in one orbit, by first writing the distance from the Earth to the Sun in standard form.**

b) **Calculate the average speed of the Earth as it orbits the Sun in metres per second. (There are 3.16×10^7 seconds in a year.)**

Circumference = $2 \times \pi \times$ radius (p.34).
Speed = distance ÷ time.

1 *Convert the distance between the Earth and the Sun into standard form.*

You want to write 150 000 000 000 m in the form $A \times 10^n$.
A needs to be between 1 and 10, so $A = 1.5$.
The decimal place has moved 11 places to the left, so $n = 11$.

$$150\ 000\ 000\ 000\ \text{m} = 1.5 \times 10^{11}\ \text{m}$$

Sandra didn't believe in using standard form in physics. Or in plumbing.

2 *Use your calculator to find the distance the Earth travels in one orbit.*

The distance the Earth travels is just the circumference of a circle with a radius of 1.5×10^{11} m.

$$\text{Circumference} = 2 \times \pi \times \text{radius} = 2 \times \pi \times (1.5 \times 10^{11}) = 9.424... \times 10^{11}$$
$$= 9.4 \times 10^{11}\ \text{m (to 2 s.f.)}$$

Give your answer to an appropriate number of significant figures (see p.3).

3 *Calculate the Earth's speed.*

You know the Earth takes 3.16×10^7 seconds to complete an orbit. You can use this value together with the distance you found in step 2 to calculate the Earth's average speed.

$$\text{speed} = \text{distance} \div \text{time} = (9.424... \times 10^{11}) \div (3.16 \times 10^7) = 29\ 825.24...$$
$$= 30\ 000\ \text{ms}^{-1}\ \text{(to 2 s.f.)}$$

ms^{-1} is just another way of writing m/s. There's more on this on p.6.

Always use the unrounded answer in your calculation.

Your calculator will probably give you this answer in decimal form, as it's not very big. You could write this as 3.0×10^4 ms^{-1}.

Practice Questions

Q1 A current is measured as 0.00064 A. Rewrite this in standard form.

Q2 The half-life of a radioactive isotope is measured as 1.34×10^5 s. Rewrite this in decimal form.

Q3 An atom of helium has a mass of 6.65×10^{-24} g. Calculate how many atoms there are in 15 g of helium.

Q4 A current of 8.6×10^{-6} A flows through a potential difference of 25 V for 650 seconds.
Given that energy = potential difference × current × time, how much energy does the current transfer?

Q5 The North Star is approximately 4.12×10^{18} m from Earth. Given that light travels 9.5×10^{15} m a year, how many years does it take light from the North Star to reach the Earth?

Q6 A scientist is conducting an experiment using X-rays with a wavelength of 2.4×10^{-9} m.
For all waves, speed = wavelength × frequency, where speed is in metres per second (ms^{-1}), wavelength is in metres (m), and frequency is in hertz (Hz).
Given that the speed of electromagnetic waves is 3.00×10^8 ms^{-1}, calculate the frequency of the X-rays.

So, that's standard form — what about deluxe form...?

This stuff is absolutely everywhere in AS and A-level Physics — for example, most physical constants you'll use (like the speed of light or the mass of a proton) are given in standard form. Fortunately, your calculator will do most of the work for you, but make sure you understand what's going on, or you could get tripped up.

Units

Most numbers you'll deal with in physics will have units, so make sure you know what you're doing...

A *Physical Quantity* has both a *Numerical Value* and a *Unit*

A measurement without a unit is **pretty meaningless**.

For example if you were told a metal rod was '5 long', you wouldn't know if its length was:

5 millimetres:

5 centimetres:

5 inches:

5 kilometres:

◄————————————— QUITE CONSIDERABLY BIGGER THAN THIS BOOK. —————————————►

You need to make sure any quantities you have are in the **right units** before you use them in calculations.

You Need to Know Six *Base Units* and a Bunch of *Derived* Ones

Every time you state a quantity, give the **units** it is measured in.

The **Système International** (S.I.) is a set of standard units that's used around the world.
It includes a set of **base units** for physical quantities. The **S.I. base units** that you need to know are:

Quantity	S.I. base unit
mass	kilogram, kg
length	metre, m
time	second, s
current	ampere, A
temperature	kelvin, K
amount of a substance	mole, mol

Kilograms are a bit odd — they're the only S.I. unit with a scaling prefix (see p.8).

You're more likely to see temperatures given in °C.

There's also an S.I unit for luminous intensity, the candela — but you don't need to know about that one.

1) Many more units can be **derived** from these base units. Units like this are called **S.I. derived units**.

2) For example, the S.I. derived unit for **speed** is ms^{-1}. This comes from the equation speed = distance ÷ time. In the same way, the S.I. derived unit for acceleration is ms^{-2} (acceleration = change in velocity ÷ time, so it's units are $ms^{-1} \div s = ms^{-2}$). Having s to the power of –1 just means 'per second', it's the same as m/s (and s to the power of –2 means 'per second squared').

3) S.I. derived units can always be expressed **in terms of base units**, like speed is. However, some also have a **special name** and symbol. For example, the charge transferred in an electric circuit is given by the equation charge = current × time. In S.I. base units, this means the **units of charge** are equivalent to **amp-seconds**, As. But the unit of charge also has a special name — the **coulomb, C**. (1 C = 1 As). If you're working with a quantity like this you should give your answer in terms of the **special unit**, not in terms of base units.

4) You need to have a **rough idea** of the **size** of the S.I. base units and the S.I. derived units you come across in your course, so that you can **estimate quantities** using them.
There's more about estimating on pages 30-31.

The units in any equation must always be the same on both sides — this is called homogeneity of units. You can use this rule to check your equations.

Units

Worked Example 1

The unit of force is the newton, N. Force can be calculated using the equation: *force = mass × acceleration*.
Express the newton in terms of S.I. base units.

1 *Substitute units into the equation for force.*

The S.I. base unit for mass is the kilogram, kg.
The S.I. derived unit for acceleration is the metre per second squared, ms^{-2}:

As acceleration = change in velocity ÷ time
(see previous page).

Force, $N = kg \times ms^{-2}$

$1\ N = 1\ kg\,ms^{-2}$, or one kilogram metre per second squared.

Worked Example 2

The unit of energy, or work done, is the joule, J. Work done can be calculated using the equation:
work done = force applied to an object × distance the object moves.
Express the joule in terms of S.I. base units.

1 *Substitute units into the equation for work done.*

The unit of force is the newton, N.
The unit of distance is the metre, m:

Work done, $J = N \times m$

$1\ J = 1\ Nm$

2 *Convert the force into S.I. base units.*

Newtons, N, aren't S.I. base units. You know from Worked Example 1 that $1\ N = 1\ kg\,ms^{-2}$:

$J = Nm = kg\,ms^{-2} \times m = kg\,m^2s^{-2}$

$1\ J = 1\ kg\,m^2s^{-2}$, or 1 kilogram metre squared per second squared.

Group together like terms —
you multiply by *m* twice, so
you get m^2.

You can calculate the unit of energy, or work
done, in other ways, for example by using the
equation: kinetic energy = ½ × (mass × velocity²).

Practice Questions

Q1 Give the S.I. unit of:
  a) temperature,   b) mass,   c) current.

Q2 Give the S.I. derived unit of:
  a) area,   b) volume.

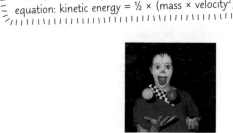

As everyone knows, the
S.I. unit for creepiness
is the clown.

Q3 Density is given by the formula *density = mass ÷ volume*. What is the unit of density, in terms of S.I. base units?

Q4 The Planck constant, *h*, is a fundamental constant (like the speed of light, *c*). It can be calculated
  using the equation *h = wavelength × momentum*. Given that wavelength is a length, and that
  momentum = mass × velocity, what is the unit of the Planck constant, in terms of S.I. base units?

To be honest, I prefer treble units...

*Make sure you learn the table of S.I. base units on page 6, and that you know how to derive units in terms of
S.I. base units. There are loads of S.I. derived units in physics, so it's best if you just try to learn them as you go.*

Converting Units

You often need to convert quantities into different units for equations, or just to make them easier to handle.

Quantities in Physics come in a **Huge Range** of **Sizes**

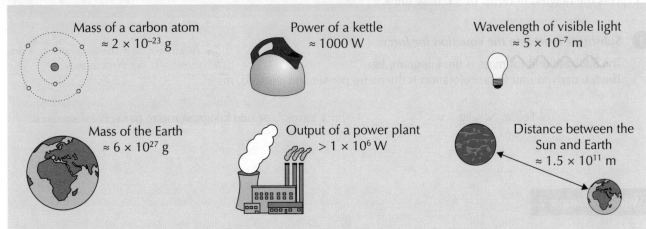

Mass of a carbon atom
$\approx 2 \times 10^{-23}$ g

Power of a kettle
≈ 1000 W

Wavelength of visible light
$\approx 5 \times 10^{-7}$ m

Mass of the Earth
$\approx 6 \times 10^{27}$ g

Output of a power plant
$> 1 \times 10^{6}$ W

Distance between the Sun and Earth
$\approx 1.5 \times 10^{11}$ m

Prefixes are scaling factors that can help you to write numbers across this range without using standard form.

There are **Scaling Prefixes** for Large and Small Quantities

Prefixes go in front of the unit name.

These are the prefixes you need to know:

For small quantities:

prefix	femto (f)	pico (p)	nano (n)	micro (μ)	milli (m)	centi (c)	deci (d)
multiple of unit	1×10^{-15}	1×10^{-12}	1×10^{-9}	1×10^{-6}	$0.001(1 \times 10^{-3})$	$0.01(1 \times 10^{-2})$	$0.1(1 \times 10^{-1})$

For large quantities:

prefix	kilo (k)	mega (M)	giga (G)	tera (T)
multiple of unit	1000 (1×10^{3})	1×10^{6}	1×10^{9}	1×10^{12}

These are the **scaling factors** for moving from the prefixed unit to the regular unit.

1) To **add** the prefix to the unit, **divide** by the scaling factor.

2) To **remove** the prefix from the unit, **multiply** by the scaling factor.

There are two ways of moving between units with **different prefixes**. You can:

1) First convert your quantity into the **regular unit** (i.e. the unit with no prefix) then convert it into the unit with the **prefix you want**.

   For example — to convert a distance from mm into km:
   First convert from **millimetres** to **metres** by multiplying by the scaling factor for mm (1×10^{-3}).
   Then convert from **metres** to **kilometres** by dividing by the scaling factor for km (1×10^{3}).

2) Convert between the units **directly** by finding an **overall scaling factor**.

   Using the same example:
   Divide the scaling factor for mm (1×10^{-3}) by the scaling factor for km (1×10^{3}).
   This gives you an **overall scaling factor** of (1×10^{-3}) $\div$ (1×10^{3}) $= 1 \times 10^{-6}$.
   You then need to **multiply** your distance in mm by this overall scaling factor to get the distance in km.

See p.23 for more about working with indices like this.

It's easy to get muddled when you're converting between units, but there's a general rule to check your answer:

- If you're moving to a **larger** unit (e.g. g to kg) then the number gets **smaller**.
- If you're moving to a **smaller** unit (e.g. cm to mm) then the number gets **bigger**.

This is true for **all** unit conversions (like the ones on p.10), not just the prefixed units here.

Converting Units

Worked Example 1

If you're a bit unsure about standard form, flick back to page 4.

Convert 1625 microseconds into milliseconds, by first converting into seconds.

1 *Convert into seconds.*

From the table on the previous page, $1 \text{ μs} = 1 \times 10^{-6}$ s, so:

You're removing a prefix, so multiply by the scaling factor.

$$1625 \text{ μs} \times (1 \times 10^{-6}) = 1.625 \times 10^{-3} \text{ s}$$

2 *Convert into milliseconds.*

From the table, $1 \text{ ms} = 1 \times 10^{-3}$ s.

$$(1.625 \times 10^{-3} \text{ s}) \div (1 \times 10^{-3}) = \mathbf{1.625 \text{ ms}}$$

You're adding a prefix, so divide by the scaling factor.

You're moving to a larger unit, and the number has become smaller, so this looks right.

Worked Example 2

Convert 0.354 gigajoules into megajoules by converting directly between the units.

1 *Find the overall scaling factor to move from gigajoules to megajoules.*

$1 \text{ GJ} = 1 \times 10^9$ J and $1 \text{ MJ} = 1 \times 10^6$ J, so the overall scaling factor to move from GJ to MJ is:

If you're not sure about whether to divide (1×10^9) by (1×10^6) or the other way around, think about the size of each unit — 1 MJ is smaller than 1 GJ, so you'd expect your scaling factor to be bigger than 1 for your number to increase.

$$(1 \times 10^9) \div (1 \times 10^6) = 1 \times 10^3$$

2 *Convert into megajoules.*

Multiply by the scaling factor you found in step 1.

You're moving to a smaller unit, and the number has become larger, so this looks right.

$$0.354 \text{ GJ} \times (1 \times 10^3) = \mathbf{354 \text{ MJ}}$$

Volumes and *Areas* are a Bit More *Tricky*

$1 \text{ m} = 100 \text{ cm}$ **does not** mean that $1 \text{ m}^2 = 100 \text{ cm}^2$.
If a measurement is **squared** or **cubed**, then you need to do the **same** to the scaling factor.
This generally comes up with areas and volumes:

> 1)   The units of an area are **squared**, so **square** the scaling factor.
> 2)   The units of a volume are **cubed**, so **cube** the scaling factor.

E.g. to convert from m^2 to mm^2: $1 \text{ mm} = 1 \times 10^{-3} \text{ m}$ so $5 \text{ m}^2 = 5 \div (1 \times 10^{-3})^2 = 5\,000\,000 \text{ mm}^2$

To convert from dm^3 to m^3: $1 \text{ dm} = 1 \times 10^{-1} \text{ m}$ so $8 \text{ dm}^3 = 8 \times (1 \times 10^{-1})^3 = 0.008 \text{ m}^3$

Worked Example 3

Convert 6897 mm³ into dm³ by converting directly between units.

1 *Find the scaling factor to move from mm to dm.*

$1 \text{ mm} = 1 \times 10^{-3} \text{ m}$ and $1 \text{ dm} = 1 \times 10^{-1} \text{ m}$, so the scaling factor to move from mm to dm is:

$$(1 \times 10^{-3}) \div (1 \times 10^{-1}) = 1 \times 10^{-2}$$

Again, think about the size of each unit to check which number to divide by which — you're moving to a bigger unit, so you'd expect your scaling factor to be smaller than 1 for your number to decrease.

2 *Multiply the volume in mm³ by the scaling factor cubed.*

$$6897 \text{ mm}^3 \times (1 \times 10^{-2})^3 = \mathbf{6.897 \times 10^{-3} \text{ dm}^3}$$

See p.23 for how to find this without using a calculator.

Converting Units

There are a Few **Special Units** You Need to Know About

There are a few special units you may come across in your course. They're not S.I. units, and they're harder to convert to and from as you can't just multiply or divide by a multiple of ten. For example:

> **The electronvolt, eV:**
> This is a **small** unit of **energy**. An electronvolt is the work done moving an electron through a potential difference of 1 volt.
> **1 eV = 1.60 × 10⁻¹⁹ J.** To convert a quantity **from eV to J**, **multiply** by 1.60×10^{-19}, and to convert a quantity from **J to eV**, **divide** by 1.60×10^{-19}.

1.60×10^{-19} is the charge, in coulombs, on an electron. You'll be given it in your exam.

> **The kilowatt-hour, kWh:**
> This is a **large** unit of **energy**. A kilowatt-hour is the amount of energy used by a 1 kW device in 1 hour.
> **1 kWh = 3.6 × 10⁶ J.** To convert a quantity **from kWh to J**, **multiply** by 3.6×10^{6}, and to convert a quantity from **J to kWh**, **divide** by 3.6×10^{6}.

Energy = power × time, so this is 1000 W (1 kW) multiplied by the number of seconds in an hour (60 × 60).

Worked Example 4

An electron accelerated through a potential difference gains 5.5 eV of energy.
Convert this energy into joules.

1 **Decide whether to multiply or divide by the conversion factor.**

You're moving from eV to J, so you need to multiply by the conversion factor.

You're moving from a small unit (eV) to a large unit (J), so you want your number to decrease. The conversion factor is smaller than 1, so you multiply by the conversion factor.

Electronvolts are for wimps — Sandeep liked to measure his energy levels in kilowatt-hours.

2 **Do the calculation.** $5.5 \times (1.60 \times 10^{-19}) = 8.8 \times 10^{-19}$ J

A joule is much bigger than an electronvolt, so you'd expect your answer to be much smaller than the value in the question.

Practice Questions

Q1 The diameter of an atom is estimated to be about 100 pm. What is this in metres?

Q2 The diameter of a fluorine nucleus is estimated to be 7.5 femtometres. What is this in nanometres?

Q3 The mass of the Moon is 7.3×10^{16} Gg. What is this in kg?

Q4 A scientist is investigating how the volume of a gas changes with temperature. At a temperature of 30 °C, the volume of the gas is 17.3 cm³. Convert this volume into m³.

Q5 The cross-sectional area of a wire is 0.0079 cm². Convert this into an area in mm².

Q6 A photon of light hits a metal plate and transfers 3.65×10^{-19} J of energy to an electron in the metal. Convert this energy into electronvolts.

Q7 A television is left on stand-by overnight and uses 0.012 kWh of electricity. Convert this energy into joules.

I used to hate unit calculations, but I've been converted...

Make sure you understand how to decide whether to multiply or divide by a conversion factor in a calculation — it can be a bit tricky, which is why it's always a good idea to check your final answer looks sensible. And check if there are any conversion factors you need to learn for your course — you won't necessarily be given all of them in your exams.

Percentages, Fractions and Ratios

Percentages, fractions and ratios pop up a fair bit in physics, so make sure you're happy using them all.

Percentages, Fractions and Ratios let you Compare Amounts

Percentages, fractions and ratios are different ways of **expressing proportion**.

A **percentage** compares a **part** of something to a **whole**.

> Here, the potential difference across the bulb is 2 V, out of a total potential difference of 10 V in the circuit.

> The potential difference across the bulb is **20%** of the total potential difference in the circuit.

Ratios and fractions can be also used to compare a **part** of something to a **whole**, or for comparing **two numbers**.

> The potential difference across the bulb is 2 V, compared to a potential difference of 10 V from the power supply.

> The **ratio** of the potential difference across the bulb to the potential difference across the power supply is 2:10 or **1:5**.

The **fraction** of the potential difference across the power supply that acts across the bulb is $\frac{2}{10}$ or $\frac{1}{5}$.

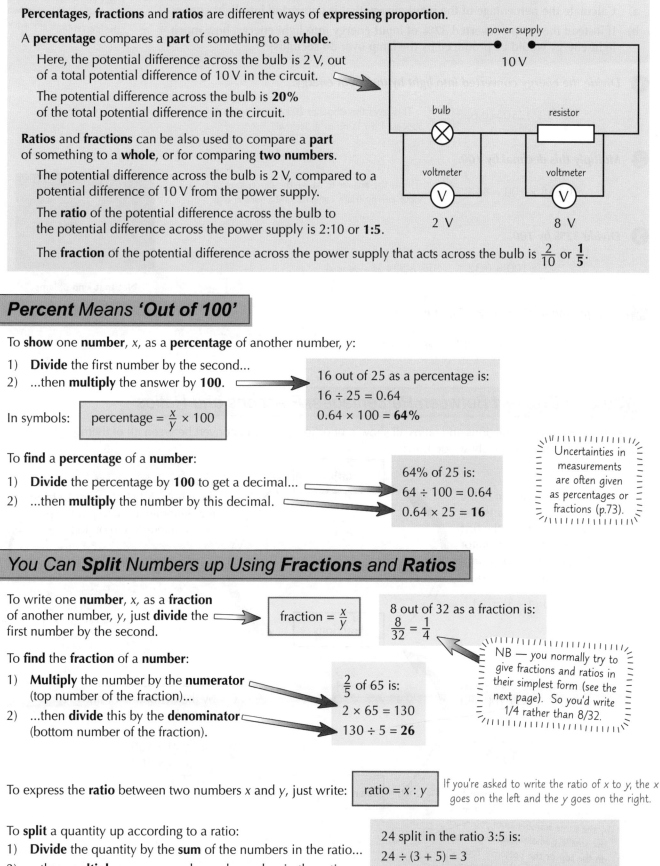

power supply
10 V
bulb
resistor
voltmeter
voltmeter
2 V
8 V

Percent Means 'Out of 100'

To **show** one **number**, x, as a **percentage** of another number, y:

1) **Divide** the first number by the second...
2) ...then **multiply** the answer by **100**.

In symbols: $\boxed{\text{percentage} = \frac{x}{y} \times 100}$

> 16 out of 25 as a percentage is:
> $16 \div 25 = 0.64$
> $0.64 \times 100 = \mathbf{64\%}$

To **find** a **percentage** of a **number**:

1) **Divide** the percentage by **100** to get a decimal...
2) ...then **multiply** the number by this decimal.

> 64% of 25 is:
> $64 \div 100 = 0.64$
> $0.64 \times 25 = \mathbf{16}$

Uncertainties in measurements are often given as percentages or fractions (p.73).

You Can Split Numbers up Using Fractions and Ratios

To write one **number**, x, as a **fraction** of another number, y, just **divide** the first number by the second.

$\boxed{\text{fraction} = \frac{x}{y}}$

> 8 out of 32 as a fraction is:
> $\frac{8}{32} = \frac{1}{4}$

To **find** the **fraction** of a **number**:

1) **Multiply** the number by the **numerator** (top number of the fraction)...
2) ...then **divide** this by the **denominator** (bottom number of the fraction).

> $\frac{2}{5}$ of 65 is:
> $2 \times 65 = 130$
> $130 \div 5 = \mathbf{26}$

NB — you normally try to give fractions and ratios in their simplest form (see the next page). So you'd write 1/4 rather than 8/32.

To express the **ratio** between two numbers x and y, just write: $\boxed{\text{ratio} = x : y}$

If you're asked to write the ratio of x to y, the x goes on the left and the y goes on the right.

To **split** a quantity up according to a ratio:

1) **Divide** the quantity by the **sum** of the numbers in the ratio...
2) ...then **multiply** your answer by each number in the ratio.

> 24 split in the ratio 3:5 is:
> $24 \div (3 + 5) = 3$
> $3 \times 3 = 9$ and $3 \times 5 = 15$, so you get **9:15**

Percentages, Fractions and Ratios

Worked Example 1

A lamp has an input energy of 1250 J over 30 seconds. It converts 835 J of this energy into useful light energy, and the rest is wasted as heat energy.

a) **Calculate the percentage of the input energy that is converted into light energy.**

b) **If instead the lamp converted 32% of input energy into light energy, how much light energy would be produced by the lamp over 30 seconds?**

The percentage of input energy that's converted into useful energy (like light) is known as the 'percentage efficiency'.

1 *Divide the energy converted into light by the input energy.*

$$835 \div 1250 = 0.668$$

This gives the efficiency (see above) of the lamp as a decimal.

2 *Multiply this decimal by 100.*

$$0.668 \times 100 = \textbf{66.8\%}$$

This is the answer to a) — the percentage of input energy that's converted into light energy.

3 *Divide 32% by 100.*

$$32 \div 100 = 0.32$$

This is 32% as a decimal.

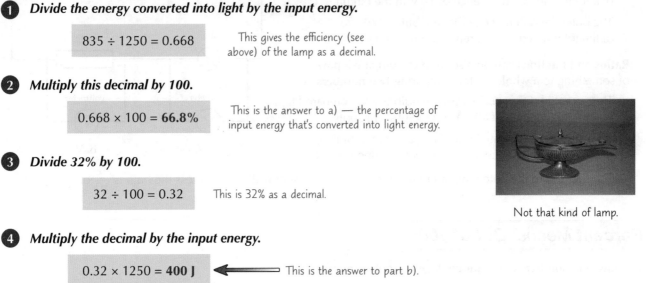

Not that kind of lamp.

4 *Multiply the decimal by the input energy.*

$$0.32 \times 1250 = \textbf{400 J}$$

This is the answer to part b).

You Can **Convert** Between Percentages, Fractions and Ratios

Because percentages, fractions and ratios all show proportions, you can convert between all of them. Here's a handy diagram to show you how:

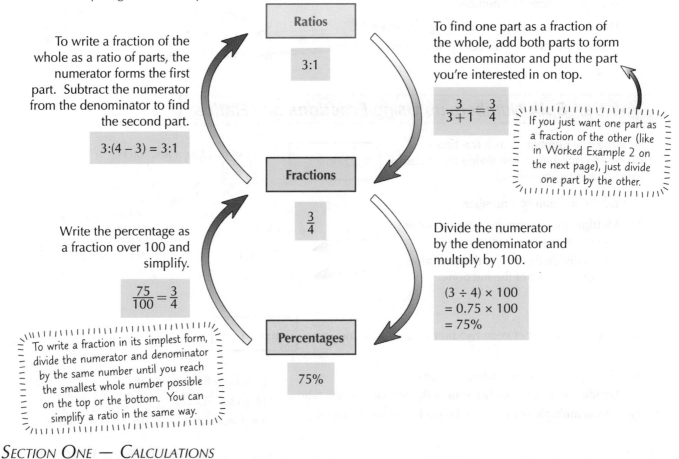

Ratios

3:1

To write a fraction of the whole as a ratio of parts, the numerator forms the first part. Subtract the numerator from the denominator to find the second part.

$$3:(4 - 3) = 3:1$$

To find one part as a fraction of the whole, add both parts to form the denominator and put the part you're interested in on top.

$$\frac{3}{3+1} = \frac{3}{4}$$

If you just want one part as a fraction of the other (like in Worked Example 2 on the next page), just divide one part by the other.

Fractions

$$\frac{3}{4}$$

Write the percentage as a fraction over 100 and simplify.

$$\frac{75}{100} = \frac{3}{4}$$

Divide the numerator by the denominator and multiply by 100.

$$(3 \div 4) \times 100$$
$$= 0.75 \times 100$$
$$= 75\%$$

To write a fraction in its simplest form, divide the numerator and denominator by the same number until you reach the smallest whole number possible on the top or the bottom. You can simplify a ratio in the same way.

Percentages

75%

Percentages, Fractions and Ratios

Worked Example 2

Transformers use two coils of wire to change the potential difference (p.d.) of a power supply. The ratio of the number of turns in the primary coil to the number of turns in the secondary coil is equal to the ratio of the potential difference across the primary coil to the potential difference across the secondary coil.

A transformer has 15 turns in its primary coil and 20 turns in its secondary coil.

a) What is the ratio of the number of turns in the primary coil to the number of turns in the secondary coil? Give your answer as a ratio in its simplest form.

b) If a potential difference of 54 V is applied across the primary coil, what will the potential difference across the secondary coil be?

metal core

P.d. in   P.d. out

primary   secondary
coil   coil

1 *Write down the ratio of the number of turns in the primary coil to the number of turns in the secondary.*

There are 15 turns in the primary coil, so this is the number on the left-hand side of the ratio, and there are 20 in the secondary coil, so this is the right-hand number in the ratio.

15 : 20

2 *Simplify the ratio.*

To get the ratio in its simplest form, divide each side by the same number until you reach the smallest whole number possible on one side.

÷ 5 $\quad$ ÷ 5
15 : 20
3 : 4

So the ratio in its simplest form is:

3 : 4

3 *Turn this ratio into a decimal.*

It'll be easier to find the potential difference across the secondary coil if the ratio is in decimal form. This is done by dividing the left-hand number by the right-hand number.

$3 \div 4 = 0.75$

4 *Write an equation involving the ratio and the potential differences.*

The ratio of the number of coils is the same as the ratio of the potential differences, so:

$$0.75 = \frac{\text{primary p.d}}{\text{secondary p.d}}$$

5 *Rearrange the equation and solve it to find the secondary potential difference.*

Multiply both sides of the equation by the secondary p.d. and divide both sides by 0.75:

$$\text{secondary p.d.} = \frac{\text{primary p.d}}{0.75} = \frac{54}{0.75} = 72$$

There's more about rearranging equations coming up on p.18-21.

So the potential difference across the secondary coil is **72 V**.

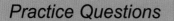

Practice Questions

Q1 A machine uses 250 J to run. Its manufacturer claims that 36% of this energy is converted into useful energy.

a) Calculate the useful energy output based on the manufacturer's claims.

b) The actual useful energy output is 45 J. Calculate the percentage of energy that is wasted.

Q2 An ultrasound wave of intensity 375 mW cm^{-2} hits a boundary and is reflected. The intensity of the reflected wave is 120 mW cm^{-2}. What fraction (in its simplest form) of the wave's intensity is reflected by the boundary?

Q3 Two resistors, A and B, are connected in series with a cell. The ratio of the potential difference (p.d.) across resistor A (V_A) to the p.d. across the cell (V_C) is the same as the ratio of the resistance of resistor A (R_A) to the total resistance of the two resistors (R_T).
Resistor A has a resistance of 4 Ω and resistor B has a resistance of 12 Ω. The p.d. across the cell is 8 V.

a) Write the ratio of the resistance of resistor A (R_A) to the total resistance of the two resistors (R_T).

b) Calculate the p.d. across resistor A.

After all that maths, I'm not feeling 100%...

You'll have probably met all of this stuff before, but it's worth checking you're happy with converting between fractions, ratios and percentages — it's quite easy to make a mistake in the conversion between fractions and ratios in particular.

Probability

A lot of things in physics are completely predictable — for example, if you apply the same force to the same object in exactly the same situation, it will always move in the same way. Other things, like radioactive decay, aren't as predictable. That's where probability *comes in.*

Probabilities Let you Make Predictions

Imagine rolling a normal, six-sided dice.

Each time you roll it, you're just as likely to get one number as another — you **can't predict** what will happen.

But if you roll the same dice again and again, you can make some general predictions.
E.g. if you rolled a dice 5 times:

You'd be **really unlikely** to get five sixes:

You'd be **unlikely** to just get ones and twos:

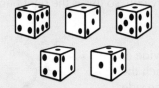

You'd be **most likely** to get a mixture of numbers:

You still can't predict what number you'd get on any one particular roll, but you can be **pretty confident** about what will happen over **many rolls**. And the **more rolls** you make, the **more confident** you can be.

This is one kind of situation where probability comes up in physics — it lets us make **predictions** about what will happen over a **large group** of **random events** that can't be predicted individually.

Probabilities are Normally Written as **Decimals** *or* **Fractions**

Probabilities tell you the **proportion** of the time that something is **likely to happen** — e.g. for rolling the dice in the example above, there are six possible outcomes that are equally likely, one of which is landing on a 6. So the probability of rolling a 6 is equal to $\frac{1}{6}$. There's more on proportions on pages 11-12.

> Probabilities are given as **numbers between 0 and 1**.
> 1) If something has a probability of **1** it is **certain** to happen.
> 2) If it has a probability of **0** it **definitely won't** happen.
> You'll generally see probabilities written as **decimals** or **fractions** (although you can also write them as percentages).

When flipping an ordinary coin, there are two possible outcomes — landing on heads or landing on tails. So the probability of it landing on heads is $\frac{1}{2}$, 0.5 or 50%.

The **larger** the probability, the **more likely** an event is going to happen. For example, the probability of not rolling a six with a six-sided dice is $\frac{5}{6}$. This is a higher probability than rolling a six ($\frac{1}{6}$) and so is more likely to happen.

Another example of probability is **radioactive decay**.

A radioactive source contains a large number of unstable **nuclei**. Each nucleus has a fixed **probability** of **decaying** (turning into a more stable nucleus).

An individual radioactive decay is **random** — it can't be predicted. But by considering a **large number** of unstable nuclei, we can make a prediction about how many unstable nuclei we **expect** to decay over a certain time — see the next page.

Against all the odds, they'd all turned up in the same outfit.
Again.

Probability

You Can Use Probabilities to Calculate **Expected Frequencies**

If an outcome has a probability of p, and there are n events, the **expected frequency** of the outcome is given by:

expected frequency = pn

If it helps — you can think of an event as an opportunity for an outcome to happen.

Just like with the dice example on p.14, the more events you calculate an expected frequency over, the more correct your expected frequency is going to be.

For example, the number of unstable nuclei that decay in a radioactive source every second is given by:

A = the **number** of unstable nuclei that decay per second (also called the **activity**).

$$A = \lambda N$$

N = **number of unstable nuclei** in the radioactive source (i.e. the number of events).

λ = the **probability** of an unstable nucleus decaying in a given second (this is called the **decay constant**).

This equation comes up in A-level Physics.

Worked Example

A radioactive source has a decay constant of 1.96×10^{-6} s^{-1}.
How many unstable nuclei are there in the source if it has an expected decay frequency of 3.0 decays per second?

1 *Write down an equation for N.*

The equation above is for the expected decay frequency (the activity).
Rearrange this to get an equation for N:

$$A = \lambda N \xrightarrow{\text{divide both sides by } \lambda} N = A \div \lambda$$

λ is the probability of an unstable nucleus decaying in a given second.

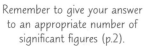

That sauce does look pretty radioactive.

2 *Substitute in the values from the question.*

$$N = A \div \lambda = 3.0 \div (1.96 \times 10^{-6}) = 1.530... \times 10^{6}$$

So there must be **1.5×10^{6} unstable nuclei** (to 2 s.f.) in the source.

Remember to give your answer to an appropriate number of significant figures (p.2).

Practice Questions

Q1 One radioactive isotope has a decay constant of 3.464×10^{-11} s^{-1} and another has a decay constant of 5.253×10^{-8} s^{-1}. A scientist has a sample of each isotope, each with the same number of unstable nuclei. Which sample will have a higher expected frequency of decay?

Q2 Fluorine-18 has a decay constant of 1.05×10^{-4} s^{-1}. Estimate how many unstable nuclei will decay each second for a sample of fluorine-18 containing 1.45×10^{25} nuclei.

Q3 A sample of a radioactive isotope contains 3.92×10^{24} unstable nuclei. Its average activity is measured as 150 decays per second. What is the probability of a nucleus of the isotope decaying in a given second?

It's probably best to have a cup of tea after all that...

Most of this stuff's fairly basic, but make sure you learn it — probabilities must be between 0 and 1, they can be given as fractions or decimals (or sometimes percentages) and the higher the probability, the more likely an event will happen.

Introduction to Equations

Equations are used all over the place in physics to describe rules and the relationships between quantities.
That means knowing how to use equations is a pretty vital skill if you want to get through this course in one piece...

Equations Show a Relationship Between Quantities

You should already be familiar with a fair few equations from GCSE, for example:

Force = mass × acceleration: $$F = ma$$

The wave equation, velocity = frequency × wavelength: $$v = f\lambda$$

Remember — "ma" just means "m × a" and "fλ" just means "f × λ".

Equations can be written out in words, or use letters to represent the different quantities.
AS and A-level Physics add a lot more equations into the mix. You'll be given a lot of them in your exams, but you should still be familiar with them all and know what to do with them.

You Need to Recognise these Symbols

Most of the symbols that you'll come across in physics will be really familiar,
but there are a few that might be new to you:

Symbol	Meaning	Where you might see it
$\approx$	'approximately equals'	The small angle approximation: $\sin\theta \approx \tan\theta \approx \theta$
$<$ or $>$	'is less than' or 'is more than'	To show that the angle of incidence for light hitting a boundary is greater than the angle of refraction: $\theta_i > \theta_r$
$<<$ or $>>$	'is much less than' or 'is much more than'	To show that the velocity, v, of an object is slower than the speed of light, c: $v << c$
$\propto$	'is directly proportional to'	Acceleration is directly proportional to force: $a \propto F$
Δ	'change in'	Acceleration is the change in velocity divided by the time the change takes: $a = \Delta v / \Delta t$
Σ	'sum of'	At equilibrium, the sum of the clockwise moments around a point is equal to the sum of the anticlockwise moments around the same point: Σ **clockwise moments** = Σ **anticlockwise moments**
$\pm$	'plus or minus'	Stating the uncertainty in something: **12 ± 0.5 g**

There's more on the small angle approximation on p.38.

There's more on working with proportionality on p.20-21.

See p.72-73.

Make Sure Quantities are in the Correct Units

1) Your quantities need to be in the **correct units** before you use them in an equation — e.g. to get a force in newtons using the equation $F = ma$, you need the mass to be in kg, and the acceleration to be in ms^{-2}.

2) The overall units on each side of an equation must be the **same**. Generally this means making sure quantities are in **S.I. base units** or **S.I. derived units** (see page 6) — although if a question asks you for an answer in **non-S.I. units** (e.g. $km\,hr^{-1}$), you may need to convert your quantities into the appropriate non-S.I. units.

3) You can **check** the units are the **same** on both sides of an equation. For example, if you want to calculate a speed in ms^{-1} using speed = distance ÷ time, the distance needs to be in metres and the time needs to be in seconds so that both sides of the equation match.

> speed = distance ÷ time
> ms^{-1} = m ÷ s

Introduction to Equations

Worked Example

The velocity of an object travelling with a constant acceleration, a, will change by Δv in a given time interval, Δt. These three values are related by the equation: $a = \frac{\Delta v}{\Delta t}$.

A car has an initial velocity of 18 kmhr⁻¹ due east and accelerates at a constant rate in this direction for 10 seconds. At the end of this time, the velocity of the car is 36 kmhr⁻¹.

Calculate the acceleration of the car during this interval, in ms⁻².

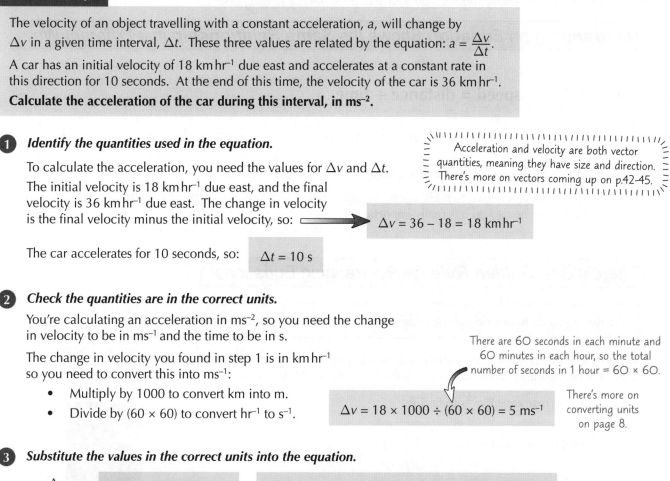

1 *Identify the quantities used in the equation.*

To calculate the acceleration, you need the values for Δv and Δt.

The initial velocity is 18 kmhr⁻¹ due east, and the final velocity is 36 kmhr⁻¹ due east. The change in velocity is the final velocity minus the initial velocity, so: ⇒ $\Delta v = 36 - 18 = 18$ kmhr⁻¹

Acceleration and velocity are both vector quantities, meaning they have size and direction. There's more on vectors coming up on p.42-45.

The car accelerates for 10 seconds, so: $\Delta t = 10$ s

2 *Check the quantities are in the correct units.*

You're calculating an acceleration in ms⁻², so you need the change in velocity to be in ms⁻¹ and the time to be in s.

The change in velocity you found in step 1 is in kmhr⁻¹ so you need to convert this into ms⁻¹:

- Multiply by 1000 to convert km into m.
- Divide by (60 × 60) to convert hr⁻¹ to s⁻¹.

There are 60 seconds in each minute and 60 minutes in each hour, so the total number of seconds in 1 hour = 60 × 60.

$\Delta v = 18 \times 1000 \div (60 \times 60) = 5$ ms⁻¹

There's more on converting units on page 8.

3 *Substitute the values in the correct units into the equation.*

$a = \frac{\Delta v}{\Delta t}$ so: $a = 5 \div 10 = 0.5$ ms⁻² **So the car has a constant acceleration of 0.5 ms⁻².**

Practice Questions

The symbol for density is a Greek letter rho (ρ) — it looks like a p but it isn't. Confusingly, it's also the symbol for resistivity.

Q1 The density of an object is given by the equation $\rho = m \div V$, where ρ = density in kgm⁻³, m = the object's mass in kg and V = the object's volume in m³. Calculate the density of an object with a mass of 4.5 kg, and a volume of 0.41 m³.

Q2 Newton's second law states that $F = \frac{\Delta (mv)}{\Delta t}$, where F is the average force acting on an object, m is the object's mass, v is the object's velocity, and t is time. If an object of mass 2.0 kg is travelling at 3.5 ms⁻¹ at $t = 5.0$ seconds, and at 4.8 ms⁻¹ in the same direction at $t = 8.5$ seconds, calculate the average force in newtons acting on the object during this time.

Q3 Resistivity is a measure of how well a material conducts electricity.
The resistivity of a material can be calculated by finding the resistance of a wire made from that material and then using the equation $\rho = RA \div L$, where ρ is the resistivity of the material in Ωm, R is the resistance of the wire in Ω, A is the cross sectional area of the wire in m² and L is the length of the wire in m.

A copper wire of length 0.45 m and a diameter of 1.2 mm has a resistance of 6.7×10^{-3} Ω.

a) Calculate the cross-sectional area of the wire in m².
(Hint — you can assume the wire is a cylinder of diameter 1.2 mm. The area of a circle = πr^2.)

b) Calculate the resistivity of the copper the wire is made from.

Exam grades — proportional to the amount of revision done...

This may all seem quite basic, but equations will come up in pretty much every maths question in your physics exams (and in a lot of the questions in this book), so you really need to know your stuff. If you struggled with any of the questions, it's worth looking back over these pages to make sure that this all makes sense before you move on.

Working with Equations

Sometimes you'll get a nice question like the ones on page 17, where the quantity you're after is on one side of the equation on its own. Normally though, you'll have to do some rearranging first.

Rearranging an *Equation* Shows the *Same Relationship* in a *Different Way*

You know that:

speed = distance ÷ time

You can also say:

distance = speed × time

and:

time = distance ÷ speed

These equations all show the **same relationship**, they've just been **rearranged**.

Most of the time, you'll have to rearrange an equation before you use it, so making sure you're comfortable with how to do it is **really important**.

There's One *Golden Rule* for Rearranging Equations

Whatever you do to **one side** of the equation, you need to do to the **other side** of the equation.

This includes things like adding, subtracting, multiplying, dividing, as well as trickier things like squaring, taking a square root or a logarithm (see pages 24-26 for this last one).

For example, to rearrange $R = \frac{V}{I}$ to find I:

1) **Multiply** both sides by I:

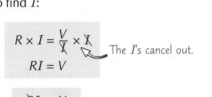

$$R \times I = \frac{V}{\cancel{I}} \times \cancel{I}$$

The I's cancel out.

$$RI = V$$

2) **Divide** both sides by R:

The R's cancel out.

$$\frac{\cancel{R}I}{\cancel{R}} = \frac{V}{R}$$

So: $\implies$ $I = \frac{V}{R}$

Similarly, the golden rule for snappy dressing is 'there's no outfit that isn't improved by the right hat'.

If you need to rearrange an equation, you should normally do this **before** you substitute in your values. It can be a bit trickier to rearrange an equation once you've substituted all the numbers into it.

If You Take a *Square Root*, there are *Two Answers*

A quadratic equation is an equation that's in the form $ax^2 + bx + c = 0$, (where a, b, and c are just numbers.)

If you've got a quantity **squared** in an equation, you might need to take a **square root** — for example, when solving a quadratic equation.
Every positive number has two square roots — a **positive root** and a **negative root**.
(Your calculator will probably only give you the positive one.)

For example, the square roots of 16 are **4** and **–4**. This is because: $4^2 = 4 \times 4 = 16$
and: $(-4)^2 = (-4) \times (-4) = 16$
You could show this by writing: $\sqrt{16} = \pm 4$. See p.16 for a reminder about the ± symbol.

Sometimes, you'll only need to consider **one answer** — e.g. if you've got an equation involving time squared (t^2) and you want to find t, negative time is pretty meaningless so you'll want the positive answer.

Sometimes though, **both** answers are meaningful — if you're taking a square root to find a displacement, the sign gives you the displacement's direction (remember — vectors like displacement have a **size** and a **direction**, p.42). You would then need to decide from the question which direction the displacement is in and use this to work out whether the displacement is positive or negative.

Working with Equations

The force due to gravity between two objects is given by: $F = \dfrac{Gm_1m_2}{r^2}$, where m_1 is the mass of the first object, m_2 is the mass of the second object, r is the distance between their centres, and G is a constant. $G = 6.67 \times 10^{-11} \, N\,m^2\,kg^{-2}$.

If the force due to gravity between two objects is 1.00×10^{-6} N, and the masses of the objects are 1230 kg and 2450 kg, what is the distance between their centres?

1 *Identify the quantity that you need to find.*

You want the distance between the masses, which is r.

2 *Rearrange the equation to get r on its own.*

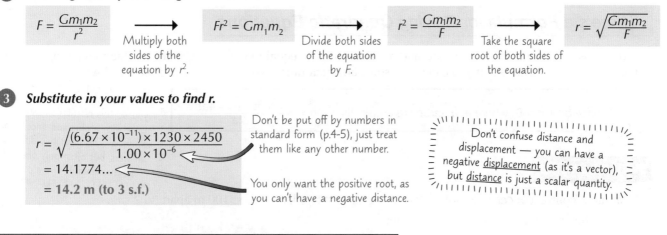

$$F = \frac{Gm_1m_2}{r^2}$$

Multiply both sides of the equation by r^2.

$$Fr^2 = Gm_1m_2$$

Divide both sides of the equation by F.

$$r^2 = \frac{Gm_1m_2}{F}$$

Take the square root of both sides of the equation.

$$r = \sqrt{\frac{Gm_1m_2}{F}}$$

3 *Substitute in your values to find r.*

$$r = \sqrt{\frac{(6.67 \times 10^{-11}) \times 1230 \times 2450}{1.00 \times 10^{-6}}}$$

$$= 14.1774...$$

$$= 14.2 \text{ m (to 3 s.f.)}$$

Don't be put off by numbers in standard form (p.4-5), just treat them like any other number.

You only want the positive root, as you can't have a negative distance.

Don't confuse distance and displacement — you can have a negative displacement (as it's a vector), but distance is just a scalar quantity.

Some Equations are a Bit **Tricky** to Rearrange

$s = ut + \tfrac{1}{2}at^2$ is one of the **equations of motion** for an object moving with constant acceleration. s = displacement, u = initial velocity, a = acceleration and t = time.

This is known as a **quadratic equation** as it has a t^2 term in it (p.20). You might be given this equation and asked to find t. Unless $u = 0$ (i.e. the object starts at rest), finding t is a bit tricky, as you **can't** get t on it's own on one side of the equation. If $s = 0$, you've just got some slightly more complicated rearranging to do — see the example below.

A ball is thrown straight up with an initial velocity of 8.5 ms^{-2}. Its acceleration due to gravity is -9.81 ms^{-2}.

What is the total time, in seconds, for the ball to reach its maximum height and then fall back to its starting height?

1 *Identify the quantity you want to find.*

Here you're after t, the time the ball takes to return to its starting height.

2 *Substitute in $s = 0$:* $0 = ut + \tfrac{1}{2}at^2$

$s = 0$ because the ball starts and finishes at the same height, so the total displacement is zero.

3 *Rearrange the equation.*

If you multiply two numbers together and get zero, one of the two must be equal to zero. So rearrange the equation so that it's two expressions, each containing t, multiplied together to give zero.

$$0 = ut + \tfrac{1}{2}at^2$$

$$0 = t(u + \tfrac{1}{2}at)$$

On the right hand side of the equation, both parts have t in them, so you can factorise the equation (rewrite it with brackets).

4 *Find the solutions.*

There are two ways that $t(u + \tfrac{1}{2}at)$ can be equal to zero (i.e. there are two solutions).

$$t = 0 \qquad \text{or} \qquad u + \tfrac{1}{2}at = 0$$

This corresponds to when the ball is thrown.

This corresponds to the time the ball takes to fall back to its starting height. This is the solution you want.

Working with Equations

5 *Rearrange $u + \frac{1}{2}at = 0$ to get t on its own.*

$$u + \frac{1}{2}at = 0 \longrightarrow \frac{1}{2}at = -u \longrightarrow at = -2u \longrightarrow t = -\frac{2u}{a}$$

Subtract u from both sides of the equation.

Multiply both sides of the equation by 2.

Divide both sides of the equation by a.

6 *Substitute your values in to find t.*

From the question, $u = 8.5$ ms^{-1}, $a = -9.81$ ms^{-2}.

$$t = -\frac{2 \times 8.5}{-9.81} = \frac{17}{9.81} = 1.732... = \textbf{1.7 s (to 2 s.f.)}$$

There's a **Formula** for Solving **Quadratic Equations**

If you're asked to find t in $s = ut + \frac{1}{2}at^2$ and **neither** s or u are **equal to 0**, you **might not be able** to rearrange to find t. Luckily, there's a **formula** that you can use to solve **any quadratic** if you write it out in a **standard** way:

If $ax^2 + bx + c = 0$, where a, b and c are constants, then $x = \dfrac{-b \pm \sqrt{b^2 - 4ac}}{2a}$

The plus or minus sign means you do this calculation twice — once with a plus and once with a minus. This gives two different answers, but often only one will be meaningful — see p.18.

Worked Example 3

A car has a constant acceleration of 1.5 ms^{-2}. It goes past two lamp posts, 100 m apart (to 2 s.f.). It passes the first lamp post at a speed of 15 ms^{-1}.

Calculate the time taken for the car to travel between the two lamp posts.

1 *Identify the quantity you want to find and the quantities you know.*

Here you're after t again, and you know $u = 15$ ms^{-1}, $s = 100$ m (to 2 s.f.) and $a = 1.5$ ms^{-2}.

2 *Substitute the values into $s = ut + \frac{1}{2}at^2$ and rearrange into a standard quadratic equation.*

½ × 1.5 = 0.75

$$100 = 15t + 0.75t^2 \longrightarrow 0 = 0.75t^2 + 15t - 100$$

$a = 0.75$ $b = 15$ $c = -100$

3 *Substitute a, b and c into the quadratic formula.*

$$t = \frac{-15 \pm \sqrt{15^2 - (4 \times 0.75 \times -100)}}{2 \times 0.75} = 5.27... \text{ or } -25.27...$$

So the time taken for the car to travel between the two lamp posts is **5.3 s (to 2 s.f.)**

You're only interested in the positive answer, because you can't have negative time.

Proportional Relationships can be Written as **Equations**

If you're told that two quantities are **directly** or **inversely proportional**, then you can write down their relationship as an equation.

$\propto$ means 'is directly proportional to' (see p.16).

If y is **directly proportional** to x, this can be written: $y \propto x$ which means: $y = kx$ (where k is a constant)

If y is **inversely proportional** to x, this can be written: $y \propto \frac{1}{x}$ which means: $y = \frac{k}{x}$ (where k is a constant)

You can calculate the value of k if you know one pair of values for x and y. You can then use this value of k to find y at another value of x (and vice versa).

Working with Equations

Stars give off light with a range of wavelengths. The most common (peak) wavelength of the light from any star (called λ_{max}) is inversely proportional to the surface temperature (T) of the star.

Star A has a surface temperature of 8500 K and the light it produces has a peak wavelength of 3.41×10^{-7} m. If star B has a surface temperature of 7500 K, what is the peak wavelength of the light produced by star B?

1 *Write an equation for the relationship.*

λ_{max} is inversely proportional to T, so you can write: $\quad \lambda_{max} \propto \dfrac{1}{T} \quad$ and therefore: $\quad \lambda_{max} = \dfrac{k}{T} \quad$ — k is a constant that is the same for all stars.

2 *Rearrange the equation to get k on its own.* $\quad \lambda_{max} = \dfrac{k}{T} \quad \xrightarrow{\text{Multiply both sides by } T.} \quad T\lambda_{max} = k$

3 *Calculate the value of k.*

$T\lambda_{max} = k$ is a relationship that's true for **all stars**.

The units on both sides of the equation need to match (see p.16), so the units of the constant k are m K (metre kelvins). Be careful, they're not millikelvins.

Using the data for star A, calculate k: $\quad k = T_A \times \lambda_{max, A} = 8500 \times 3.41 \times 10^{-7} = 2.8985 \times 10^{-3} \text{ mK}$

T_A means the temperature of star A.

$\lambda_{max, A}$ means the peak wavelength of the light from star A.

4 *Use this value of k to find the peak wavelength of the light emitted by star B.*

$\lambda_{max, B}$ means the peak wavelength of the light from star B.

$\lambda_{max, B} = \dfrac{k}{T_B} = \dfrac{2.8985 \times 10^{-3}}{7500} = 3.864... \times 10^{-7}$

T_B means the temperature of star B.

So the peak wavelength of the light from star B, $\lambda_{max, B} = 3.9 \times 10^{-7}$ m (to 2 s.f.)

Practice Questions

Q1 The final velocity of an object travelling at constant acceleration can be calculated from $v = u + at$, where u and v are the initial and final velocities (in ms^{-1}), a is the acceleration (in ms^{-2}) and t is the time taken (in s) to change from velocity u to velocity v. A car is travelling at 15 ms^{-1}. Calculate how long it would take to reach a velocity of 22 ms^{-1} if it had a constant acceleration of 0.80 ms^{-2}.

Q2 A trolley is launched onto a track with an initial velocity of 2.0 ms^{-1}. It experiences constant deceleration of -0.8 ms^{-2} and stops after 2.5 m. Calculate the time it takes to come to a stop.

Q3 The relationship between the force, F, on a spring and the extension, ΔL, of the spring is $F \propto \Delta L$. A spring has an extension of 0.025 m when a force of 16 N is applied to it. The force on the spring is removed and a new force of 28 N is applied to the spring. Calculate the new extension of the spring.

Q4 The electric force between two charged particles is given by the equation $F = \dfrac{1}{4\pi\varepsilon_0}\dfrac{Q_1 Q_2}{r^2}$ where Q_1 and Q_2 are the charges on the two particles (in C), r is the distance between them (in m), and ε_0 is a constant, with a value of 8.85×10^{-12} Fm^{-1}. If the force between two electrons (each with a charge of -1.60×10^{-19} C) is 2.6×10^{-11} N, what is the distance between them?

I don't work with equations, equations work for me...

Rearranging equations is a fairly fundamental skill for AS and A-level physics, so make sure you know what you're doing. It's a good idea to rearrange equations one variable at a time as in these examples, rather than trying to sort everything out at once, particularly if you aren't very comfortable with algebra, as you're less likely to make mistakes.

Inverse Functions and Index Laws

A few odds and ends on these two pages to help you with equations and calculations. Dig in.

Every Function Has an **Inverse**

The **inverse** of a function is its **opposite** — for example, **dividing** is the inverse of **multiplying**, and **subtracting** is the inverse of **adding**.

If you were to apply one function to a number (e.g. multiplying by 2), and then apply its inverse function to the answer (e.g. dividing by 2), you would end up with the original number.

$$y \times 2 = 2y$$

$$2y \div 2 = y$$

Use Inverse Functions to **Rearrange Calculations**

This table shows some of the functions and their inverses that you're likely to meet in your course.

Function	add	multiply	square	cube	sin	cos	tan	taking the exponential of a number	raising ten to the power of a number
Inverse	subtract	divide	square root	cube root	$\sin^{-1}$	$\cos^{-1}$	$\tan^{-1}$	taking the natural log of a number	taking the log base ten of a number

These four are probably very familiar to you.

There's more about these three on pages 36-39.

There's more about these two on pages 24-29.

You can **undo** the effect of a function by applying the **inverse function**. This lets you rearrange and solve equations (see p.18-21).

For example: If $x^3 = 125$, $x = \sqrt[3]{125} = 5$ If $\cos \theta = 0.5$, $\theta = \cos^{-1} 0.5 = 60°$

Apart from the common ones like multiply and divide, a lot of functions **share a button** on your calculator with their **inverse**. To use the inverse function, press **shift** (or second function, depending on your calculator), then the **function button**.

For example, to use $\cos^{-1}$ you'd press: shift   then   cos

The inverse function will be written in **small letters** by the button, like this: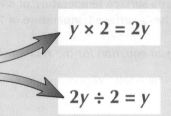

Worked Example

A current-carrying wire in a magnetic field experiences a force. The size of the force, *F*, in newtons (N), is given by $F = BIL \sin \theta$, where *B* is the strength of the magnetic field in tesla (T), *I* is the current in amps (A), *L* is the length of the wire in metres (m) and θ is the angle between the field and the current.

A wire of length $L = 0.12$ m, carrying a current of $I = 4.5$ A, is placed in a magnetic field of strength $B = 2.2 \times 10^{-5}$ T. It experiences a force of $F = 8.0 \times 10^{-6}$ N. Calculate θ, the angle between the magnetic field and the wire.

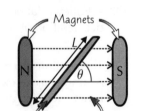

Wire, carrying current *I*.

Magnetic field, strength *B*.

1 **Rearrange the equation to get sin θ on its own.**

Divide both sides by *BIL*.

$$F = BIL \sin \theta \longrightarrow \frac{F}{BIL} = \sin \theta \longrightarrow \sin \theta = \frac{F}{BIL}$$

Sin θ is currently multiplied by *BIL*, so to get sin θ on its own, you need to perform the inverse function. The inverse of multiplying is dividing, so divide both sides by *BIL*.

It's easier to keep track of what's going on if you swap the sides of the equation around, so the thing you want to find is on the left.

Inverse Functions and Index Laws

2 *Take the inverse sine of both sides of the equation.* sin^{-1} is the inverse of sin, so $\sin^{-1}(\sin\theta) = \theta$.

$$\sin\theta = \frac{F}{BIL} \longrightarrow \sin^{-1}(\sin\theta) = \sin^{-1}\left(\frac{F}{BIL}\right) \longrightarrow \theta = \sin^{-1}\left(\frac{F}{BIL}\right)$$

3 *Substitute in the values from the question to find θ.*

There's more on significant figures (s.f.) on p.2-3.

$$\theta = \sin^{-1}\left(\frac{8.0\times10^{-6}}{2.2\times10^{-5}\times4.5\times0.12}\right) = \sin^{-1}0.6734... = 42.330...°$$

$\theta = 42°$ (to 2 s.f.)

The **Index Laws** Help you to Work with **Powers**

A number with an **index** (also known as a **power**) tells you **how many times** the number is multiplied by itself. For example: $8^3 = 8\times8\times8$

If a number has a **negative** index, that just means it's **1 over** the number multiplied by itself. E.g. $8^{-3} = \dfrac{1}{8\times8\times8}$

For a number that is to the power of a **fraction**, the **denominator** is the **root** of the number and the **numerator** tells you what **power** the root is raised to. E.g. $8^{\frac{3}{4}} = (\sqrt[4]{8})^3 = \sqrt[4]{8}\times\sqrt[4]{8}\times\sqrt[4]{8}$

If you're working with an equation where the **same number** is raised to a power more than once, there are a few **laws** you'll need to follow:

When **multiplying**, add the indices:	When **dividing**, subtract the indices:	When **raising** one power to **another**, multiply the two indices together:
$x^2 \times x^5 = x^{(2+5)} = x^7$	$y^{15} \div y^3 = y^{(15-3)} = y^{12}$	$(z^2)^3 = z^{(2\times3)} = z^6$

Be careful though — you can **only** use these rules if the numbers that you're working with have the **same base** (that's the large number at the bottom).

See p.4-5 for more on standard form.

You can use these rules to do standard form calculations without a calculator. For example:

$(4\times10^3)\times(2\times10^5) \longrightarrow (4\times2)\times(10^3\times10^5) \longrightarrow 8\times(10^3\times10^5) \longrightarrow 8\times10^8$

Put the numbers and the powers of ten next to each other.　Multiply the numbers.　Add the powers.

$(6\times10^6)^2 \longrightarrow 6^2\times(10^6)^2 \longrightarrow 36\times(10^6)^2 \longrightarrow 36\times10^{12} \longrightarrow 3.6\times10^{13}$

Get rid of the brackets.　Square the number.　Multiply the power by 2.　Rewrite in standard form.

Practice Questions

Q1 Without using a calculator, find $(8\times10^4)\div(2\times10^{-2})^2$.

Q2 A mass hanging from a spring is pulled down 0.15 m from its rest position and released, so that it bounces up and down. The displacement, x (in m) of the mass from its rest position after time t (in s) from its release is given by the equation: $x = A\cos\omega t$, where A and ω are constants.

Given that $A = -0.15$ m and $\omega = 5.5$ s^{-1}, at what time after being released will the mass first reach a displacement of 0.10 m?

To use this equation, your calculator needs to be in radians mode — see page 36.

spring

displacement = O m

mass

The mass moves up and down around this line. Points below this line have a negative displacement, and points above it have a positive displacement.

I prefer my functions in the chorus...

Make sure you can find all the functions in the table on page 22 on your calculator and that you know how to use them. Nothing worse than a calculator malfunction mid-exam. (Well, there's that dream I keep having, where I'm sat in the middle of the exam hall and I realise I'm not wearing any... Ahem, yes well, moving on...)

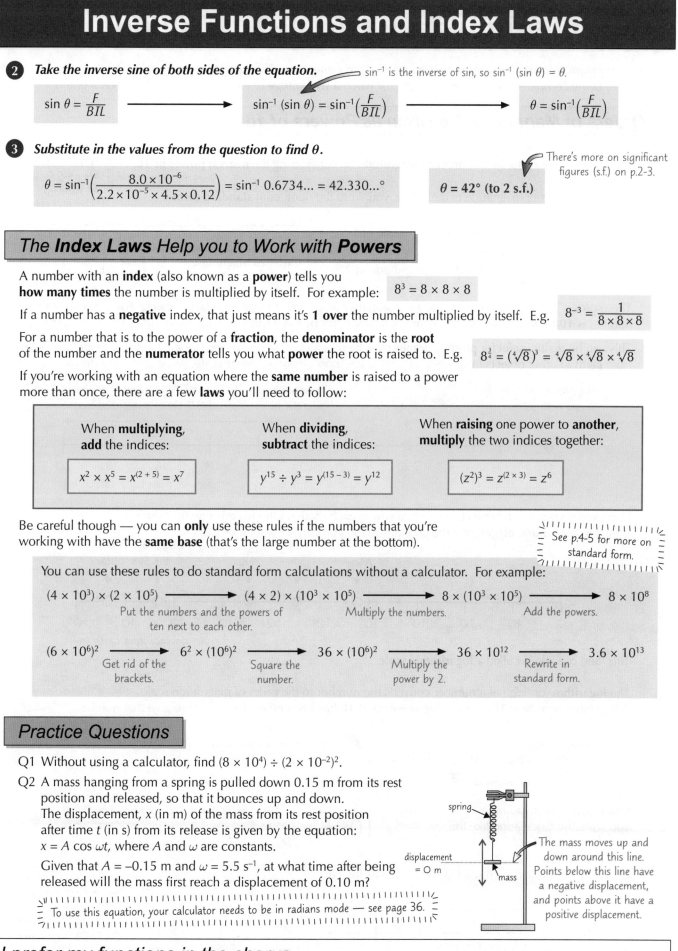

Logarithms and Orders of Magnitude

Orders of magnitude and *logarithms* are two sides of the same coin. They tend to crop up when really large values are being compared to really small values, or when a wide range of values are being plotted on a graph.

Orders of Magnitude Are Given as Powers of 10

Numbers can be related to an **order of magnitude** by considering the **nearest power of 10**.

See p.4-5 for more on standard form.

To find the order of magnitude of a number, you write the number in **standard form**.

For example: $25 = 2.5 \times 10^1$,
so 25 has an order of magnitude of **1**.

$250 = 2.5 \times 10^2$,
so 250 has an order of magnitude of **2**.

Power of Ten	10^1	10^2	10^3	10^4
Order of Magnitude	1	2	3	4

These orders of magnitude can be used to **compare** numbers that range over **large scales**. For example, if one number is **100 000 times** bigger than another, they differ by **five** orders of magnitude (since $10^5 = 100\,000$).

This can be really useful for **plotting graphs** over large scales. E.g. if you were looking at the average distances from Earth to other objects in space, and plotted them on a normal, **linear scale**, you'd end up with:

The Moon and Sun would both be here ↓   Pluto ↓   The closest star to the Sun is 2000 pages to the right and the North Star is 200 000 pages to the right

O 2 4 6 8 10 12 14 16 18 20

distance from Earth (billion km)

However, if you plot the objects on a scale where each mark on the scale is one (or more) **orders of magnitude bigger** than the previous mark, you can see a lot more:

Moon ↓   Sun ↓   Pluto ↓   Closest star to the Sun ↓   North Star ↓

O 10^2 10^4 10^6 10^8 10^{10} 10^{12} 10^{14} 10^{16} 10^{18} 10^{20}

distance from Earth (m)

This kind of scale is called a **logarithmic scale**.

The **logarithm** (or 'log') of a number converts the number to the order of magnitude scale.
A logarithm with **base 10** tells you the **power that 10 has been raised to** in order to give that number.

This small number just tells you what the base is.

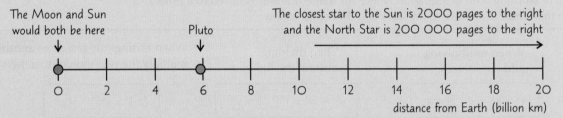

$$\log_{10}(y) = x$$

x is the power that ten is raised to, to make *y*.

You can take logs with other bases too — p.27-29.

Remember, when you raise 10 to a power, you write the calculation like this:

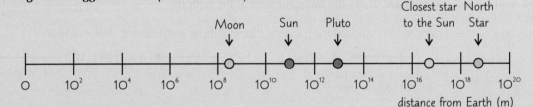

$$10^x = y$$

This means multiply 10 by itself *x* times.

E.g. $10^3 = 10 \times 10 \times 10 = 1000$

Normally in physics you'll see $\log_{10}(x)$ written as **log (x)**.

Check whether you need to know how to use logarithms for your exams — you might not if you're doing AS Physics.

y	15	25	35
log (y) (to 2 d.p.)	1.18	1.40	1.54

Log (35) = 1.54, so $10^{1.54} = 35$

Taking the log base ten of a number, and raising ten to the power of a number are **inverse functions** (see page 22).

Logarithms and Orders of Magnitude

Use Your **Calculator** to Find the Log of a Number

Your calculator should have a button like this: ⟹ log

This will give you the log to **base ten** of whatever number you enter after you press it.
You might need to put **brackets** around whatever you're taking the log of.

Your calculator should also have a button like this: ⟹ 10^x

This will give you ten to the power of whatever number you enter after you press it.

This may be a 'second function' on your calculator, so you may have to press shift or second function first.

There are Some **Useful Rules** for Working with Logs

Because 10^x and log (x) are **inverse functions**:
These are **basic rules** for working with logarithms.

$$10^{(\log x)} = x \quad \text{and} \quad \log (10^x) = x$$

There are **three** other rules that make dealing with logs easier:

$$\log (xy) = \log (x) + \log (y) \qquad \log \left(\tfrac{x}{y}\right) = \log (x) - \log (y) \qquad \log (x^k) = k\log (x)$$

There are also a couple of logs that are useful to remember:

$$\log (10) = 1 \quad \text{and} \quad \log (1) = 0$$

This is true because any number raised to the power of 0 is equal to 1.

Follow These Special **Significant Figure Rules** When Working with Logs

1) If you take the log of a number, you **shouldn't** use the significant figure rule on page 3.
   Instead, you should give your answer to the **same number of decimal places** (d.p.)
   as there are **significant figures** in the number you're taking the log of. For example:

   There is **1 significant figure** in the number 50. log (50) = 1.6989... = 1.7 to **1 decimal place**.
   There are **4 significant figures** in the number 3.425. log (3.425) = 0.53466... = 0.5347 to **4 decimal places**.

2) If you **raise ten** to a power, you should give your answer to the same number of **significant figures** as there are **decimal places** in the power. For example:

   There is **1 decimal place** in the number 0.6. $10^{0.6}$ = 3.9810... = 4 to **1 significant figure**.
   There are **2 decimal places** in the number 3.24. $10^{3.24}$ = 1737.800... = 1700 to **2 significant figures**.

Worked Example 1

The decibel scale measures intensity level — how loud we perceive sound to be. The loudness, IL, in decibels (dB), is related to the intensity of the sound being heard, I, and the constant I_0, by the formula $IL = 10\log \left(\tfrac{I}{I_0}\right)$.
If a sound has an intensity of 0.009 Wm^{-2}, what is its loudness in decibels? The value of I_0 is 1.0×10^{-12} Wm^{-2}.

1 **Identify the quantity you want to find.**

You're after the loudness. $IL = 10\log \left(\tfrac{I}{I_0}\right)$, so you don't have to do any rearranging.

2 **Substitute the values into the equation and do the calculation.**

You can type this all into your calculator in one go. Be careful with the brackets.

$$IL = 10\log \left(\frac{0.009}{1.0\times10^{-12}}\right) = 99.542... = \textbf{99.5 dB (to 1 d.p.)}$$

The intensity of the sound is given to 1 s.f., so I/I_0 only has 1 s.f. too. This means you'd give the final answer to 1 d.p.

Logarithms and Orders of Magnitude

Worked Example 2

The magnitude of a star is a measure of its brightness. There are two kinds of magnitude: apparent magnitude, m, which is the brightness of a star when viewed from Earth, and absolute magnitude, M, which is a measure of how much light a star is giving out. The two are related by the equation $m - M = 5 \log \left(\frac{d}{10}\right)$, where d is the distance from Earth to the star, measured in parsecs (a parsec is a large unit of distance used in astronomy).

A star has an apparent magnitude of +2.8 and an absolute magnitude of +1.2. Calculate how far from Earth it is, in parsecs, by first rearranging to get an equation for log (d).

NB. — You can have negative apparent and absolute magnitudes too.

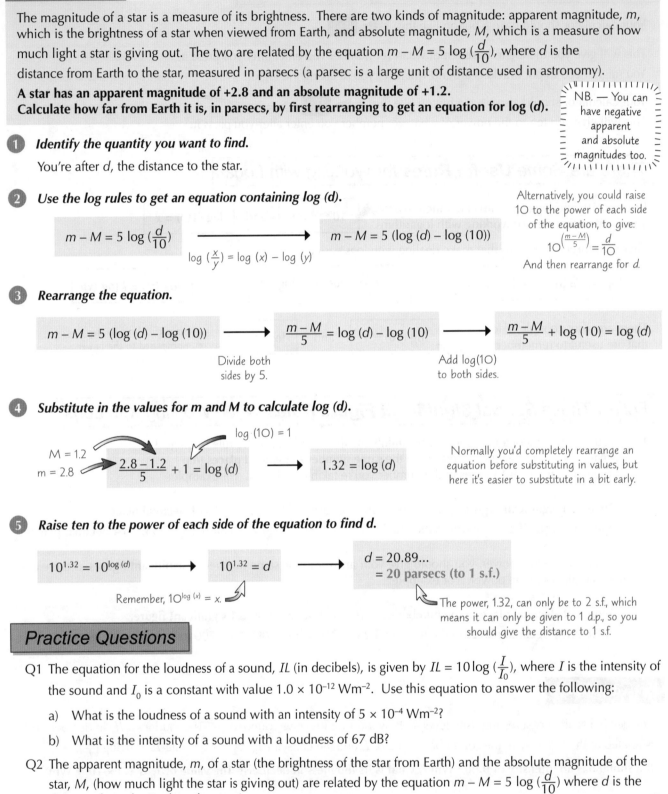

1 *Identify the quantity you want to find.*

You're after d, the distance to the star.

2 *Use the log rules to get an equation containing log (d).*

$$m - M = 5 \log \left(\frac{d}{10}\right) \xrightarrow{\log \left(\frac{x}{y}\right) = \log (x) - \log (y)} m - M = 5 (\log (d) - \log (10))$$

Alternatively, you could raise 10 to the power of each side of the equation, to give:

$$10^{\left(\frac{m-M}{5}\right)} = \frac{d}{10}$$

And then rearrange for d.

3 *Rearrange the equation.*

$$m - M = 5 (\log (d) - \log (10)) \longrightarrow \frac{m - M}{5} = \log (d) - \log (10) \longrightarrow \frac{m - M}{5} + \log (10) = \log (d)$$

Divide both sides by 5.

Add log(10) to both sides.

4 *Substitute in the values for m and M to calculate log (d).*

$\log (10) = 1$

$M = 1.2$
$m = 2.8$

$$\frac{2.8 - 1.2}{5} + 1 = \log (d) \longrightarrow 1.32 = \log (d)$$

Normally you'd completely rearrange an equation before substituting in values, but here it's easier to substitute in a bit early.

5 *Raise ten to the power of each side of the equation to find d.*

$$10^{1.32} = 10^{\log (d)} \longrightarrow 10^{1.32} = d \longrightarrow \begin{array}{l} d = 20.89... \\ = 20 \text{ parsecs (to 1 s.f.)} \end{array}$$

Remember, $10^{\log (x)} = x$.

The power, 1.32, can only be to 2 s.f., which means it can only be given to 1 d.p., so you should give the distance to 1 s.f.

Practice Questions

Q1 The equation for the loudness of a sound, IL (in decibels), is given by $IL = 10 \log \left(\frac{I}{I_0}\right)$, where I is the intensity of the sound and I_0 is a constant with value 1.0×10^{-12} Wm^{-2}. Use this equation to answer the following:

a) What is the loudness of a sound with an intensity of 5×10^{-4} Wm^{-2}?

b) What is the intensity of a sound with a loudness of 67 dB?

Q2 The apparent magnitude, m, of a star (the brightness of the star from Earth) and the absolute magnitude of the star, M, (how much light the star is giving out) are related by the equation $m - M = 5 \log \left(\frac{d}{10}\right)$ where d is the distance from the Earth to the star, in parsecs.

a) A star 96 parsecs from Earth has an apparent magnitude of +1.60. Calculate the star's absolute magnitude.

b) A star has an apparent magnitude of +1.3 and an absolute magnitude of –3.9.
   How far is it from Earth, in parsecs?

I think I need a lie down after that...

Logs are pretty tricky, but if it makes you feel any better, the maths on these pages (and the next three on natural logs) is about as hard as it's going to get. If you're struggling, just take a deep breath and go over it again.

Natural Logs and Exponentials

Unfortunately for you, logs with a base of ten aren't the only ones you need to know about...

Natural Logs are to Base e

You only need to know this stuff if you're doing the A-level course.

You'll come across some situations in physics where the **rate of change** of a quantity is **proportional** to the **size** of the quantity, e.g.:

1) The **rate of radioactive decay** is proportional to the **number of undecayed nuclei** in a sample.

2) The **rate of discharge** of a **capacitor** is proportional to the **charge remaining** on the capacitor.

A capacitor is a circuit component that stores charge.

Relationships where the rate of change of a quantity is proportional to the value of that quantity are called **exponential relationships**. The ones you'll come across in A-level physics all have the **same general form**:

1) If a radioactive source has an initial number of undecayed nuclei, N_0, the number of undecayed nuclei remaining, N, at time t since it began decaying is: $\Longrightarrow$ $N = N_0 e^{-\lambda t}$

2) A capacitor with an initial charge Q_0 will have a charge Q at time t since it began discharging: $\Longrightarrow$ $Q = Q_0 e^{\frac{-t}{RC}}$

λ, R and C are all constants.

If you plotted a graph of N against t, it would look like this: A graph of Q against t would look the same.

The **e** in these equations is a **special constant** that crops up in lots of relationships. It's equal to about 2.7183, although like π, it goes on forever. It's stored in your calculator.

It's helpful to take the **logarithm** of quantities that follow this sort of relationship, either to **calculate values** of other parts of the equation, (like R or C in the example on p.29), or to **plot** the results of an experiment on more helpful axes (see page 60).

For equations like this, it's more useful to take the logarithm to the **base e** rather than base 10 (as on p.24-26). This is called the **natural log** of a number, and is written **ln**.

You Can do Calculations Involving e and In Using Your Calculator

To raise e to a power, press: $\Longrightarrow$ e^x then enter the power.

This may be a 'second function' on your calculator, so you may have to press shift or second function first.

To take the natural log of a number, press: $\Longrightarrow$ ln then enter the number you want the log of.

You can think of ln as an abbreviation of "log natural" if it helps you to remember the difference between log and ln.

Just like with log (x) and 10^x, you need to be careful with **brackets**.

Natural logs follow the **same rules** for significant figures and decimal places as logs to base ten (see page 25):
1) If you take the natural log of a number, give your answer to the **same number of decimal places** as there are **significant figures** in the number. For example: $\ln(3.42) = 1.2296... = 1.230$ (to 3 d.p.).
2) If you're **raising e** to the power of a number, give your answer to the same number of **significant figures** as there are **decimal places** in the power. For example: $e^{-5.4} \times 10^{-3} = 4.5165... = 5 \times 10^{-3}$ (to 1 s.f.).

Natural Logs and Exponentials

Natural Logs Follow *Similar Rules* to Base Ten Logs

Just like base ten logs, e^x and $\ln(x)$ are **inverse functions**. This means:

$$e^{(\ln x)} = x \quad \text{and} \quad \ln(e^x) = x$$

The other three rules for base ten logs **also apply** to natural logs:

$$\ln(xy) = \ln(x) + \ln(y) \qquad \ln\left(\frac{x}{y}\right) = \ln(x) - \ln(y) \qquad \ln(x^k) = k\ln(x)$$

Like with base ten logs, there are a couple of natural logs that are worth remembering:

$$\ln(e) = 1 \quad \text{and} \quad \ln(1) = 0$$

Worked Example 1

The number of undecayed nuclei, N, remaining in a sample of a radioactive isotope after time t (in seconds) is given by the equation: $N = N_0 e^{-\lambda t}$, where λ is a property of the isotope and has units s^{-1}, and N_0 is the initial number of undecayed nuclei. A sample initially contains 5.60×10^{23} undecayed nuclei. For this substance, $\lambda = 1.80 \times 10^{-9}\ s^{-1}$.
Calculate the number of undecayed nuclei remaining after 7.50×10^6 seconds.

1 *Identify the quantity you want to find.*

You're after N, the number of undecayed nuclei remaining at time t.

$N = N_0 e^{-\lambda t}$, so you don't have to do any rearranging.

2 *Substitute the values into the equation and do the calculation.*

$$N = (5.60 \times 10^{23}) \times e^{-(1.80 \times 10^{-9} \times 7.50 \times 10^6)}$$
$$= (5.60 \times 10^{23}) \times e^{-0.0135}$$
$$= 5.5249... \times 10^{23} \text{ nuclei}$$

It's easier to break this calculation into stages, as the power is pretty complicated.

3 *Work out the significant figures.*

You need to look at how many significant figures your value of N_0 gives you, and how many your value of $e^{-\lambda t}$ gives you.

$$N_0 = 5.60 \times 10^{23}$$

This value is given to **three significant figures**.

The number of significant figures you can give for a number in the form e^x is equal to the number of **decimal places in the power** (see previous page). In this equation, the power is equal to $-\lambda t$.

$$-\lambda t = -(1.80 \times 10^{-9} \times 7.50 \times 10^6) = -0.0135 \text{ (to 3 s.f.)}$$

This number is given to 3 s.f. as λ and t are given to 3 s.f. — this means it has four decimal places, so the $e^{-\lambda t}$ term has **four significant figures**.

The normal rule (from p.3) for calculating significant figures kicks in here — N_0 is given to fewer significant figures than $e^{-\lambda t}$ so you'd give your answer to the same number of significant figures as N_0 — three.

$$N = 5.52 \times 10^{23} \text{ nuclei (to 3 s.f.)}$$

Natural Logs and Exponentials

Worked Example 2

The amount of charge, Q, stored on a capacitor at time t after it begins charging is given by $Q = Q_0 (1 - e^{\frac{-t}{RC}})$, where Q_0 is the charge on the capacitor when fully charged. R and C are constants.

A capacitor initially holds no charge, but can hold a total charge of 3.0×10^{-4} C. After being charged for 0.5 seconds, it holds 2.4×10^{-4} C of charge. Calculate RC for this capacitor, in s.

1 *Identify the quantity you want to find.*

You're after RC. This is in the power that e is raised to, so you'll need to do some rearranging.

2 *Start rearranging the equation.*

First, get $e^{\frac{-t}{RC}}$ on its own:

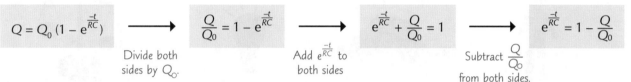

$$Q = Q_0 (1 - e^{\frac{-t}{RC}}) \longrightarrow \frac{Q}{Q_0} = 1 - e^{\frac{-t}{RC}} \longrightarrow e^{\frac{-t}{RC}} + \frac{Q}{Q_0} = 1 \longrightarrow e^{\frac{-t}{RC}} = 1 - \frac{Q}{Q_0}$$

Divide both sides by Q_0. · Add $e^{\frac{-t}{RC}}$ to both sides · Subtract $\frac{Q}{Q_0}$ from both sides.

3 *Take the natural log of both sides of the equation.*

$$\ln (e^{\frac{-t}{RC}}) = \ln (1 - \frac{Q}{Q_0}) \longrightarrow \frac{-t}{RC} = \ln (1 - \frac{Q}{Q_0})$$

The natural log of e^x is x.

You could substitute in the values from the question before taking the natural log if you wanted — but you'd still need to do some rearranging.

4 *Rearrange to get RC on its own.*

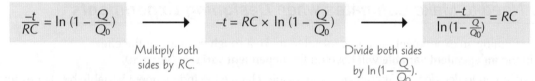

$$\frac{-t}{RC} = \ln (1 - \frac{Q}{Q_0}) \longrightarrow -t = RC \times \ln (1 - \frac{Q}{Q_0}) \longrightarrow \frac{-t}{\ln(1 - \frac{Q}{Q_0})} = RC$$

Multiply both sides by RC. · Divide both sides by $\ln (1 - \frac{Q}{Q_0})$.

5 *Substitute in the values from the question to find RC.*

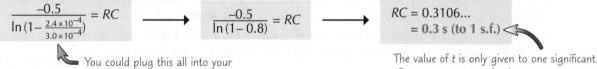

$$\frac{-0.5}{\ln (1 - \frac{2.4 \times 10^{-4}}{3.0 \times 10^{-4}})} = RC \longrightarrow \frac{-0.5}{\ln (1 - 0.8)} = RC \longrightarrow \begin{array}{l} RC = 0.3106... \\ = 0.3 \text{ s (to 1 s.f.)} \end{array}$$

You could plug this all into your calculator in one go if you wanted to.

The value of t is only given to one significant figure, so you can only give your answer to one significant figure.

Practice Questions

Q1 Use the equation for a charging capacitor given in Worked Example 2 above, and the equation for a discharging capacitor, $Q = Q_0 e^{\frac{-t}{RC}}$, to answer these questions.

a) A capacitor holding its maximum charge of 0.016 C is discharged.
Given that $RC = 0.16$ s, calculate the charge remaining on the capacitor after 0.02 seconds.

b) The capacitor is discharged completely, then recharged.
What will the charge on the capacitor be 0.04 seconds after it begins recharging?

Q2 A radioactive source contains $N_0 = 2.40 \times 10^{23}$ undecayed nuclei at $t = 0$ seconds.
After $t = 550$ seconds, the number of undecayed nuclei remaining in the source, N, has fallen to 1.50×10^{23}.
Using the equation $N = N_0 e^{-\lambda t}$, find the value of λ for this radioactive source.

Natural logs — trees that don't wear make-up...

Natural logs and exponential functions are a bit horrid maths-wise, but (like with most things in physics) once you've practised them a bit more, they'll become easier to deal with. Make sure you remember all the rules given at the top of page 28 — they're basically the same as the base 10 log rules, so if you know those, you're laughing.

Estimating

When you can't measure or calculate something accurately, estimating can be really handy.

An **Estimate** is an **Approximate Value** of a Quantity

Estimates are useful when it's either **not possible** to be accurate (for example when you're working with something that's **hard to measure** or can't be measured **directly**), or when a rough value is all that's required.

You need to have an idea of the **size** of the **different units** (p.6-7) you come across in physics, so that you can make estimates using them. For example:

A person is about 1.8 m tall.

A car travels at around 20 ms⁻¹ (about 40 mph).

The wavelength of visible light is around 500 nm.

There are (very roughly) 1×10^{22} atoms in a gram of a substance.

Estimates can be useful to **quickly check** a calculated value — for example, for long complicated equations it's quite easy to type something wrong into your calculator. If you estimated certain values within the equation so that you could do the calculation in your head, you could quickly check if your answer from the calculator seems reasonable compared to the estimate you worked out.

You May Need to Make **Estimates** when **Designing Experiments**

1) Before performing an experiment, it can be useful to make a **rough estimate** of the effect a change in the **independent variable** will have on the **dependent variable** (see p.50).

2) This can help you to decide what **increments** you should change the independent variable by. For example:

> If you're investigating how the **resistance of a wire** changes with its **length**, you might estimate that the resistance of a short 1 cm length of the wire would be **pretty small** — maybe of the order of microohms.
>
> This means it would be sensible to increase the length of the wire in **bigger steps** (say 10 cm), so that the change in resistance is **large enough to be detected** by your equipment.

Some Quantities **Can't** be Measured Accurately

1) There are some quantities that **can only be estimated**. For example:

> You can't measure the diameter of an atom **directly** — atoms don't have a fixed edge, and even if they did, there's no easy way to measure distances on that scale.
>
> Instead, the diameters of atoms are **estimated** (either by **diffracting X-rays** between atoms, or from the **number of atoms** that can fit in a **known volume**).
>
> This means that **any calculation** you do using the diameter or radius of an atom can only give you an **estimated value** as well.

If you're asked to find the area under a curved graph, you'll typically only find an estimate of the area. There's more on working with graphs on pages 68-71.

2) Estimating quantities often involves making **simplifying assumptions** about a situation, e.g. assuming an atom is a sphere to find its volume.

3) Sometimes, you'll only need to make estimates or comparisons to the nearest **order of magnitude** (p.24). This is generally the case with quantities that are very hard to estimate or that show a lot of variation.

Estimating

Worked Example

The radius of an atom is of the order of 1×10^{-10} m, and the radius of the nucleus of an atom is of the order of 1×10^{-15} m.

Estimate, to the nearest order of magnitude, the proportion of the volume of an atom that is made up by the nucleus.

Laura estimated that she had 10 seconds before her cat attacked her.

1 **Assume both the atom and its nucleus are spheres.**

This means you can find their volumes.
The volume of a sphere is given by: ⟹ $\frac{4}{3}\pi r^3$

See page 32 for more on geometry.

2 **Write down an expression for finding the volume of a nucleus as a proportion of the volume of an atom.**

You can express one number as a proportion of another by dividing one number by the other.

You want the volume of the nucleus as a proportion of the volume of the atom, so the volume of the nucleus goes on the top and the volume of the atom goes on the bottom (see p.11).

This means the radius of the atom.

This means the radius of the nucleus.

$$\frac{\frac{4}{3}\pi r_{nucleus}^3}{\frac{4}{3}\pi r_{atom}^3}$$

$\frac{4}{3}\pi$ is on the top and bottom of the expression, so it cancels out.

$$\frac{r_{nucleus}^3}{r_{atom}^3}$$

3 **Substitute in the values from the question to get your answer.**

$$\frac{r_{nucleus}^3}{r_{atom}^3} = \frac{(1\times10^{-15})^3}{(1\times10^{-10})^3} = 1 \times 10^{-15}$$

The proportion of the volume of an atom that is made up by the nucleus is approximately 1×10^{-15}, to the nearest order of magnitude.

Practice Questions

Q1 A spherical party balloon is filled with water.
  a) Estimate the volume of the balloon. The volume of a sphere is given by $\frac{4}{3}\pi r^3$, where r is the radius of the sphere.
  b) Estimate the mass of the balloon when filled with water. The density, ρ, of a substance is given by $\rho = \frac{m}{V}$, where m is the mass of the substance and V is the volume.
     (Hint: the density of water is approximately 1 g cm^{-3})

Q2 A student is investigating what happens to the length of a spring when different masses are suspended from the spring. She uses a ruler with mm increments to measure the length of the spring. A 25 g mass causes the spring to extend by about a mm. Suggest a suitable increment for her to increase the mass by between measurements.

Q3 The Earth's mass is roughly five hundred times greater than Pluto's mass, and its radius is about five times Pluto's radius. The velocity, v, necessary for an object to escape the gravitational field of an object with mass M and radius r is given by the equation: $v = \sqrt{\frac{2GM}{r}}$. G is a constant. Roughly how many times faster does an object need to be travelling to escape from Earth's gravitational field than to escape from Pluto's gravitational field? (Hint —you can approach this question in a similar way to the Worked Example above.)

Estimating — not the same as guessing...

Don't get sloppy if a question asks you to estimate something — you can't just pull a number out of the air. You need to make sure that your estimate is as accurate as you can make it, and you need to understand all of the assumptions that your estimate makes (like assuming atoms and nuclei are spheres in the example above).

Area, Surface Area and Volume

Time for a quick geometry primer...

Physics Uses **Simple Shapes** to **Model** Systems and Objects

Lots of the things you'll work with in physics are either simple shapes, or can be **approximated** as simple shapes.

A straight length of wire is approximately a **cylinder**.

You can model atoms as **spheres**.

The orbits of planets around the Sun are roughly **circular**.

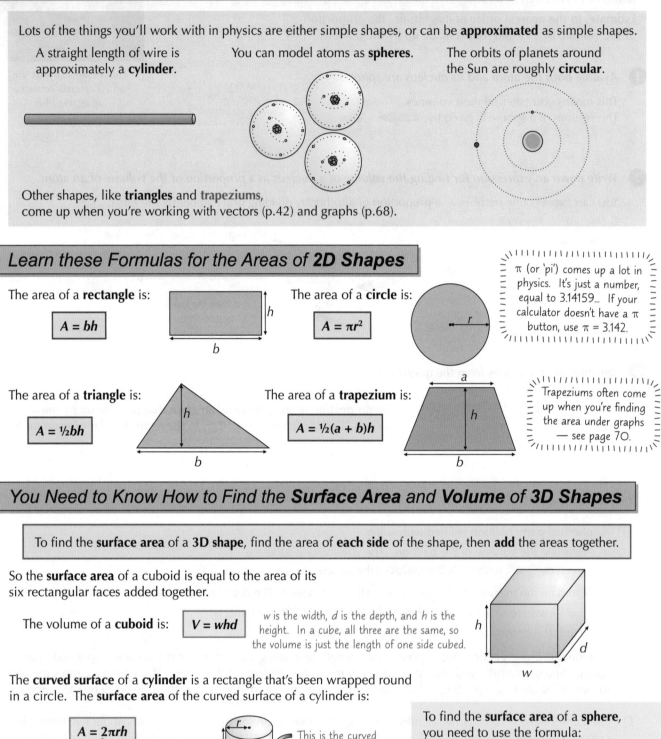

Other shapes, like **triangles** and **trapeziums**, come up when you're working with vectors (p.42) and graphs (p.68).

Learn these Formulas for the Areas of **2D Shapes**

The area of a **rectangle** is:

$$A = bh$$

The area of a **circle** is:

$$A = \pi r^2$$

> π (or 'pi') comes up a lot in physics. It's just a number, equal to 3.14159... If your calculator doesn't have a π button, use π = 3.142.

The area of a **triangle** is:

$$A = \tfrac{1}{2}bh$$

The area of a **trapezium** is:

$$A = \tfrac{1}{2}(a + b)h$$

> Trapeziums often come up when you're finding the area under graphs — see page 70.

You Need to Know How to Find the **Surface Area** and **Volume** of **3D Shapes**

To find the **surface area** of a 3D shape, find the area of **each side** of the shape, then **add** the areas together.

So the **surface area** of a cuboid is equal to the area of its six rectangular faces added together.

The volume of a **cuboid** is: $V = whd$ *w* is the width, *d* is the depth, and *h* is the height. In a cube, all three are the same, so the volume is just the length of one side cubed.

The **curved surface** of a **cylinder** is a rectangle that's been wrapped round in a circle. The **surface area** of the curved surface of a cylinder is:

$$A = 2\pi rh$$

$2\pi r$ is the circumference of the circle on the end of the cylinder (p.34).

This is the curved surface. If you want the full surface area of a cylinder, remember to add on the circles at both ends.

The **volume** of a cylinder is: $V = \pi r^2 h$

> The cross-section of a cylinder is a circle, so a cylinder's cross-sectional area is the area of a circle with the same radius.

To find the **surface area** of a **sphere**, you need to use the formula:

$$A = 4\pi r^2$$

The **volume** of a sphere is:

$$V = \frac{4}{3}\pi r^3$$

Area, Surface Area and Volume

A wire is made of a metal with a resistivity of 2.85×10^{-8} Ωm. The wire is 0.32 m long and has a radius of 1.0×10^{-3} m. The mass of the wire is 2.71 g.

a) Given that density = mass ÷ volume, calculate the density of the metal, in kg m^{-3}.

b) Given that resistance = (resistivity × length) ÷ cross-sectional area, calculate the resistance of the wire, in Ω.

1 *Find the volume of the wire.*

You can model the wire as a cylinder with a radius of 1.0×10^{-3} m and a length (height) of 0.32 m.

The volume of a cylinder is given by the equation: $\quad V = \pi r^2 h \quad$ *Length and height are the same thing here — which word you'd use just depends on whether the cylinder is standing on its end or lying on its side.*

So the volume of the wire is: $\quad \pi \times (1.0 \times 10^{-3})^2 \times 0.32 = 1.005... \times 10^{-6}$ m^3

2 *Calculate the density of the metal.*

Convert the mass in g to a mass in kg. $\quad 2.71 \div 1000 = 0.00271$ kg $\quad$ *There's more on converting units on page 8.*

Calculate the density. $\quad$ density = mass ÷ volume = $0.00271 \div (1.005... \times 10^{-6}) = 2695.686...$

The density of the metal is 2700 kg m^{-3} (to 2 s.f.)

3 *Find the cross-sectional area of the wire.*

The cross-section of a cylinder is a circle, so the cross-sectional area of the wire is given by: $\quad A = \pi r^2$

So the cross-sectional area of the wire is: $\quad \pi \times (1.0 \times 10^{-3})^2 = 3.141... \times 10^{-6}$ m^2

4 *Calculate the resistance of the wire.*

Just plug the values into the formula: $\quad$ resistance = (resistivity × length) ÷ cross-sectional area
$$= (2.85 \times 10^{-8} \times 0.32) \div (3.141... \times 10^{-6})$$
$$= 2.902... \times 10^{-3} \ \Omega$$

The resistance of the wire is 2.9×10^{-3} Ω (to 2 s.f.)

Practice Questions

Q1 A gold bar can be modelled as a cuboid measuring 25.0 cm by 12.0 cm by 5.0 cm. *density = mass ÷ volume*
  a) What is the surface area of the bar?
  b) Gold has a density of 19 000 kg m^{-3}. What is the mass of the bar?

Q2 An iron atom has a mass of 9.3×10^{-26} kg and can be modelled as a sphere with a radius of 1.4×10^{-10} m. Estimate the density of an iron atom.

Q3 The pressure of a gas in a sealed container at a constant temperature is inversely proportional to the container's volume. The tube in the diagram on the right contains gas at a pressure of 5.2×10^4 Pa. If the piston is depressed (pushed down the tube) by 1.5 cm, what will the new pressure in the cylinder be?

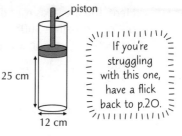

piston

25 cm

12 cm

If you're struggling with this one, have a flick back to p.20.

Stay in shape — practise your geometry...

Hopefully everything here should seem pretty familiar to you. It's all fairly straightforward, but this basic geometry can underpin a lot of the harder questions you'll come across in your physics course, so don't just skip over these pages.

Working with Angles

I know you're just dying to get stuck into the exciting topics later in this section (like trigonometry and vectors), but before you do, you need to make sure you're comfortable working with angles.

You Can Give **Angles** in **Radians or Degrees**

Radians are just another unit for measuring angles.

There are **2π radians** in a **complete circle** (that's roughly 6.28 radians).

Radians may seem like a pain, but they're really useful in a lot of the situations that are coming up on the next few pages.

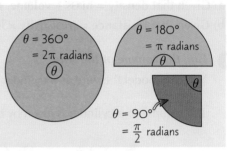

$\theta = 360°$
$= 2\pi$ radians

$\theta = 180°$
$= \pi$ radians

$\theta = 90°$
$= \frac{\pi}{2}$ radians

Converting Angles Between **Radians** and **Degrees** is **Pretty Easy**

$360° = 2\pi$ radians. So 1 degree $= \frac{2\pi}{360}$ radians.

This leads to a simple formula for **converting degrees** into **radians**:

$$\text{angle in radians} = \frac{\pi}{180} \times \text{angle in degrees}$$

To convert from **radians** to **degrees**, do the opposite:

There's more about converting units on pages 8-10.

$$\text{angle in degrees} = \frac{180}{\pi} \times \text{angle in radians}$$

For example:
An angle of 70.0° is equal to:

$70.0° = 1.22$ radians

$\frac{\pi}{180} \times 70.0 = \frac{7}{18}\pi$

$= \textbf{1.22 radians (to 3 s.f)}$

An angle of 2.00 radians is equal to:

$\frac{180}{\pi} \times 2.00 = \frac{360}{\pi}$

2.00 radians $= 115°$

$= \textbf{115° (to 3 s.f.)}$

Sometimes, you'll see angles given in radians in terms of π.
This means the answers to any calculations that use these angles will be **more exact**.

Radians are Useful for Calculating **Arc Length**

The **circumference** of a circle, **C**, is given by: $C = 2\pi r = \pi d$

(*d* is the diameter of the circle, *r* is its radius).

An **arc** is part of the circumference of a circle.

You find the **length**, **l**, of an arc by finding the fraction of the full circle the arc represents, then multiplying this by the full circle's circumference:

You're not going to make that angle joke are you? I thought not. Good.

Here, the arc goes round 180° out of a possible 360°.
So the length of the arc is:

$\frac{180}{360} \times 2\pi r = \frac{1}{2} \times 2\pi r = \pi r$

$\theta = 180°$

Here, the arc goes round 60° out of a possible 360°.
So the length of the arc is:

$\frac{60}{360} \times 2\pi r = \frac{1}{6} \times 2\pi r = \frac{1}{3}\pi r$

$\theta = 60°$

If you're working in radians, this simplifies to a **handy formula**:

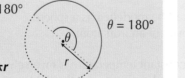

$\frac{\theta}{2\pi} \times 2\pi r = \theta r$ so: **when θ is in radians, arc length, l = θr**

Remember, $360° = 2\pi$ radians

This actually gives you the definition of one radian — it's the angle at the centre of the circle when the arc length is equal to the radius.

Working with Angles

Here are Some **Angle Rules** that Might Come in Handy

Angles in a triangle add up to 180°, or π radians.

$$A + B + C = 180°$$

Angles on a straight line add up to 180°, or π radians.

$$A + B = 180°$$

For a straight line cutting across a set of parallel lines:

Allied angles **add up to 180°**, or π radians.

$$A + B = 180°$$

Corresponding angles are equal:

Alternate angles are equal:

Vertically opposite angles are **equal**:

This stuff can be useful when dealing with vectors (p.42-49).

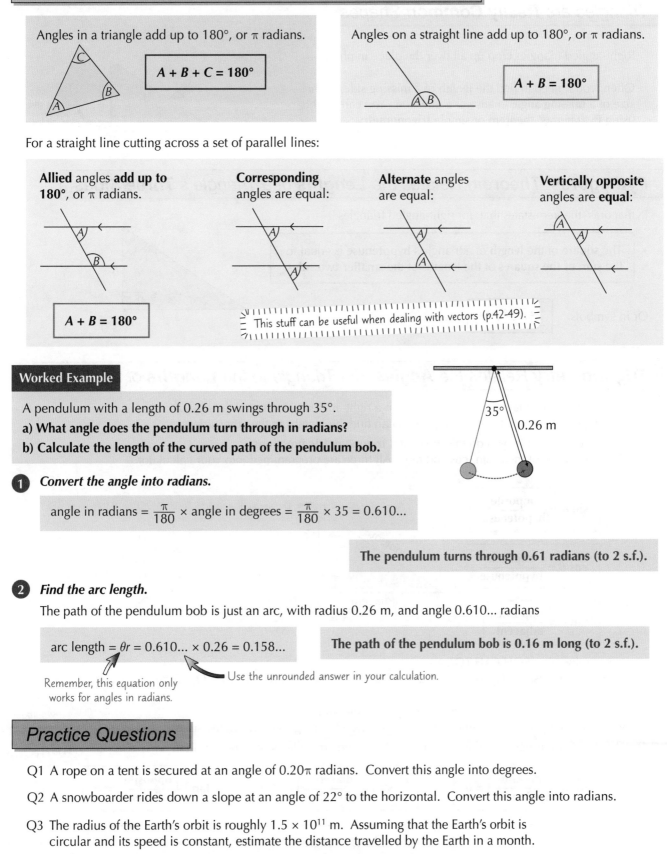

Worked Example

A pendulum with a length of 0.26 m swings through 35°.
a) What angle does the pendulum turn through in radians?
b) Calculate the length of the curved path of the pendulum bob.

1 *Convert the angle into radians.*

$$\text{angle in radians} = \frac{\pi}{180} \times \text{angle in degrees} = \frac{\pi}{180} \times 35 = 0.610...$$

The pendulum turns through 0.61 radians (to 2 s.f.).

2 *Find the arc length.*
The path of the pendulum bob is just an arc, with radius 0.26 m, and angle 0.610... radians

$$\text{arc length} = \theta r = 0.610... \times 0.26 = 0.158...$$

The path of the pendulum bob is 0.16 m long (to 2 s.f.).

Remember, this equation only works for angles in radians.

Use the unrounded answer in your calculation.

Practice Questions

Q1 A rope on a tent is secured at an angle of 0.20π radians. Convert this angle into degrees.

Q2 A snowboarder rides down a slope at an angle of 22° to the horizontal. Convert this angle into radians.

Q3 The radius of the Earth's orbit is roughly 1.5×10^{11} m. Assuming that the Earth's orbit is circular and its speed is constant, estimate the distance travelled by the Earth in a month.

Circles are really smart — they've got 360 degrees...

And two pies — they must be feeling pretty smug too. Radians seem a bit tricky, but they're just another unit, like metres and feet, or pounds and kilograms. Learn the conversion formulas on page 34 and you should be fine.

Pythagoras and Trigonometry

Knowing how to work out angles and lengths in triangles is a crucial physics skill...

Triangles are **Really Common** Shapes

Right-angled triangles crop up all over the place in physics.

Often, you'll need to find the length of a **missing side**, or the size of a **missing angle** to answer a question. You can do this using **Pythagoras' theorem** or simple **trigonometry**.

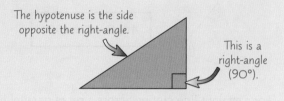

The hypotenuse is the side opposite the right-angle.

This is a right-angle (90°).

Pythagoras' Theorem Relates the **Lengths** of a Triangle's **Three Sides**

Pythagoras' theorem states that, for right-angled triangles:

> The **square** of the **length** of a triangle's **hypotenuse** is equal to the **sum of the squares** of the lengths of the **smaller two sides**.

Or in symbols: $c^2 = a^2 + b^2$ Where c is the hypotenuse.

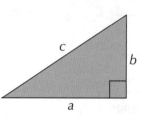

Trigonometry Relates the **Angles** in a Triangle to the **Lengths** of the Sides

1) If you know the **length** of one of the sides in a right-angled triangle and the size of one of the **angles** (other than the right angle) you can find the lengths of the other sides.

2) The functions that let you do this are called **trigonometric functions**. There are three of them: **sin**, **cos** and **tan**. All three are programmed into your calculator.

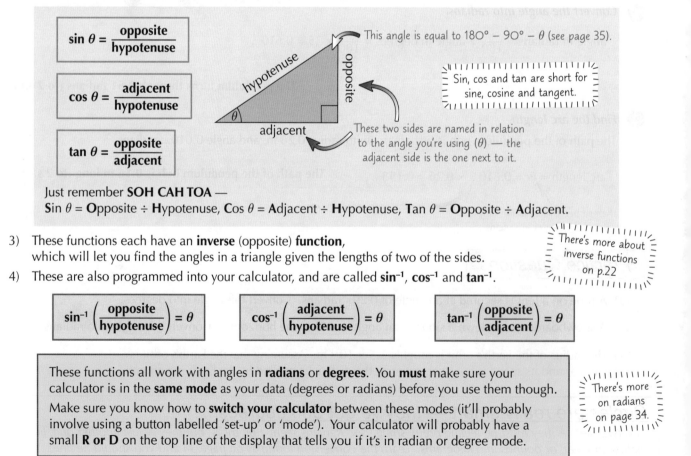

$$\sin \theta = \frac{\text{opposite}}{\text{hypotenuse}}$$

$$\cos \theta = \frac{\text{adjacent}}{\text{hypotenuse}}$$

$$\tan \theta = \frac{\text{opposite}}{\text{adjacent}}$$

This angle is equal to 180° − 90° − θ (see page 35).

Sin, cos and tan are short for sine, cosine and tangent.

These two sides are named in relation to the angle you're using (θ) — the adjacent side is the one next to it.

Just remember **SOH CAH TOA** —
Sin θ = Opposite ÷ Hypotenuse, Cos θ = Adjacent ÷ Hypotenuse, Tan θ = Opposite ÷ Adjacent.

3) These functions each have an **inverse** (opposite) **function**, which will let you find the angles in a triangle given the lengths of two of the sides.

There's more about inverse functions on p.22

4) These are also programmed into your calculator, and are called **sin⁻¹**, **cos⁻¹** and **tan⁻¹**.

$$\sin^{-1}\left(\frac{\text{opposite}}{\text{hypotenuse}}\right) = \theta$$ $$\cos^{-1}\left(\frac{\text{adjacent}}{\text{hypotenuse}}\right) = \theta$$ $$\tan^{-1}\left(\frac{\text{opposite}}{\text{adjacent}}\right) = \theta$$

These functions all work with angles in **radians** or **degrees**. You **must** make sure your calculator is in the **same mode** as your data (degrees or radians) before you use them though.

Make sure you know how to **switch your calculator** between these modes (it'll probably involve using a button labelled 'set-up' or 'mode'). Your calculator will probably have a small **R or D** on the top line of the display that tells you if it's in radian or degree mode.

There's more on radians on page 34.

Pythagoras and Trigonometry

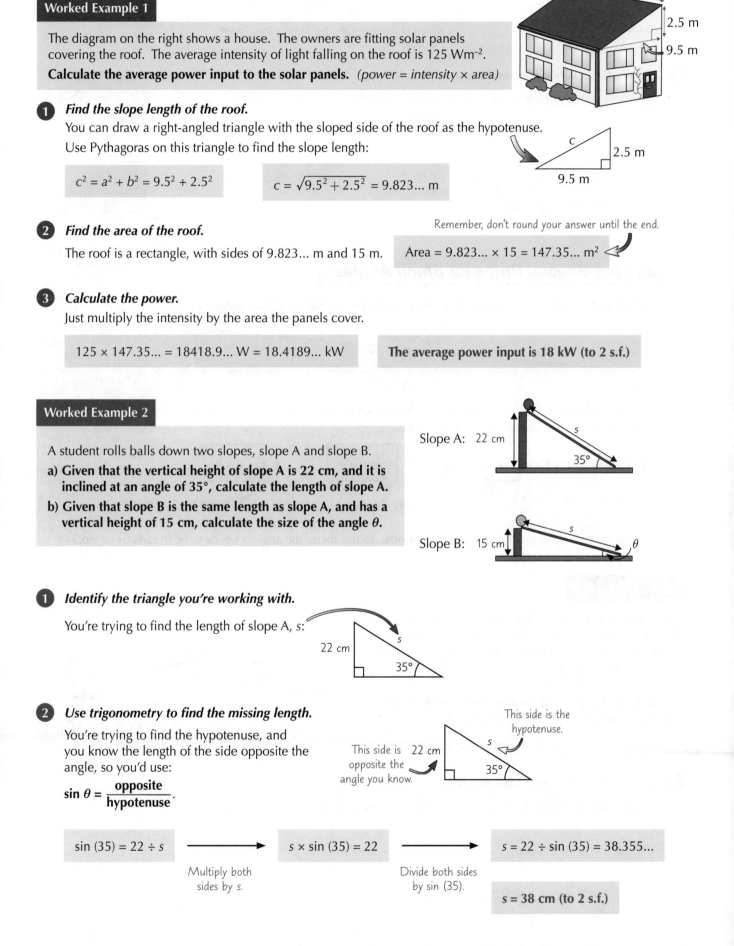

Worked Example 1

The diagram on the right shows a house. The owners are fitting solar panels covering the roof. The average intensity of light falling on the roof is 125 Wm^{-2}.
Calculate the average power input to the solar panels. *(power = intensity × area)*

15 m

2.5 m

9.5 m

1 **Find the slope length of the roof.**

You can draw a right-angled triangle with the sloped side of the roof as the hypotenuse.

Use Pythagoras on this triangle to find the slope length:

$c^2 = a^2 + b^2 = 9.5^2 + 2.5^2$

$c = \sqrt{9.5^2 + 2.5^2} = 9.823... \text{ m}$

c

2.5 m

9.5 m

2 **Find the area of the roof.**

Remember, don't round your answer until the end.

The roof is a rectangle, with sides of 9.823... m and 15 m.

Area = 9.823... × 15 = 147.35... m^2

3 **Calculate the power.**

Just multiply the intensity by the area the panels cover.

125 × 147.35... = 18418.9... W = 18.4189... kW

The average power input is 18 kW (to 2 s.f.)

Worked Example 2

A student rolls balls down two slopes, slope A and slope B.

a) Given that the vertical height of slope A is 22 cm, and it is inclined at an angle of 35°, calculate the length of slope A.

b) Given that slope B is the same length as slope A, and has a vertical height of 15 cm, calculate the size of the angle θ.

Slope A: 22 cm

s

35°

Slope B: 15 cm

s

θ

1 **Identify the triangle you're working with.**

You're trying to find the length of slope A, *s*:

22 cm

s

35°

2 **Use trigonometry to find the missing length.**

You're trying to find the hypotenuse, and you know the length of the side opposite the angle, so you'd use:

$\sin \theta = \dfrac{\text{opposite}}{\text{hypotenuse}}$.

This side is opposite the angle you know.

This side is the hypotenuse.

22 cm

s

35°

$\sin (35) = 22 \div s$

$s \times \sin (35) = 22$

$s = 22 \div \sin (35) = 38.355...$

Multiply both sides by *s*.

Divide both sides by sin (35).

$s = 38 \text{ cm (to 2 s.f.)}$

Pythagoras and Trigonometry

③ ***Draw the triangle for slope B.***

You'll need the value of s you found in step 2.

This side is opposite the angle you want to know

15 cm

$s = 38.355...cm$

This side is the hypotenuse.

θ

④ ***Identify the equation you need to use to find the angle.***

You know the side opposite the angle, and you know the hypotenuse, so you need to use: $\sin^{-1}\left(\dfrac{\textbf{opposite}}{\textbf{hypotenuse}}\right) = \theta$.

$\theta = \sin^{-1}(15 \div 38.355...) = 23.021...$

Remember, use the unrounded value.

$\theta = 23°$ (to 2 s.f.)

Trigonometry had helped Josef find the angle of the slope, but it wasn't helping him climb it.

There are **Special Rules** for **Small Angles**

1) Occasionally you'll come across situations involving very **long**, very **thin** triangles:

θ

hypotenuse

adjacent

opposite

For triangles like this, the adjacent side is almost as long as the hypotenuse.

2) When this happens, if θ is small enough (less than about 10°, or less than $\frac{\pi}{18}$ radians — see p.34), there are a few approximations you can make:

If θ is less than 10°:

$\cos\theta \approx 1$

$\sin\theta \approx \theta$

$\tan\theta \approx \theta$

So adjacent ÷ hypotenuse ≈ 1

So opposite ÷ hypotenuse ≈ θ.

So opposite ÷ adjacent ≈ θ.

3) These are called the **small angle approximations**. To use them, the angle θ needs to be in **radians** (see p.34).

Worked Example 3

Astronomers can find the distance to a nearby star by measuring the angle, θ, through which the star appears to move as the Earth orbits the Sun (as shown in the diagram — r is the radius of the Earth's orbit, about 1.5×10^{11} m).

If the angle $\theta = 3.7 \times 10^{-6}$ radians, use a small angle approximation to estimate the distance d.

d = distance to star

d

Sun

θ

Nearby star

r

$r = 1.5 \times 10^{11}$ m

Earth

① ***Draw a triangle to show what you know.***

You're trying to find d, the distance from the Sun to the star. You know θ and r.

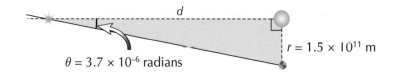

d

$r = 1.5 \times 10^{11}$ m

$\theta = 3.7 \times 10^{-6}$ radians

Pythagoras and Trigonometry

2 *Identify which small-angle approximation you should use.*

θ is tiny (3.7×10^{-6} radians is much less than $\frac{\pi}{18}$ radians),
so you can definitely use a small angle approximation.

You know the length of the side opposite the angle, and want to find the length of the side adjacent to it, so you'd use:

$$\tan \theta \approx \theta \approx \frac{\text{opposite}}{\text{adjacent}} \qquad \text{so:} \qquad \theta \approx \frac{r}{d}$$

This side is adjacent to the angle you know.

d

$\theta = 3.7 \times 10^{-6}$ radians

$r = 1.5 \times 10^{11}$ m

This side is opposite the angle you know.

3 *Rearrange the equation to find d.*

$$\theta \approx \frac{r}{d} \qquad \longrightarrow \qquad d\theta \approx r \qquad \longrightarrow \qquad d \approx \frac{r}{\theta}$$

Multiply both sides by d.

Divide both sides by θ.

$r = 1.5 \times 10^{11}$ m and $\theta = 3.7 \times 10^{-6}$ radians, so:

Remember to give your answer to an appropriate number of significant figures (see p.3).

$$d \approx (1.5 \times 10^{11}) \div (3.7 \times 10^{-6}) = 4.054... \times 10^{16}$$

$$d \approx \mathbf{4.1 \times 10^{16}\,m \text{ (to 2 s.f.)}}$$

Practice Questions

Q1 A helicopter travels 2.5 km due north, then 3.7 km due east, before flying directly back to its starting point. What is the total distance travelled by the helicopter?

Q2 A man walks along a straight path going up a hill, at an angle of 23° to the horizontal. If he walks 1.25 km along the path, what is the increase in his elevation?

Q3 The diagram on the right shows a metal rod holding a window open.
   a) What is the length of the rod?
   b) What is the angle between the window and the window frame (marked θ)?

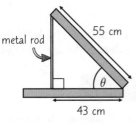

metal rod

55 cm

θ

43 cm

Q4 The diagram on the right shows a jump at a bike stunt competition.
   a) Calculate θ, the angle of inclination of the launch ramp.
   b) Calculate the difference in height between the launch ramp and the landing ramp.

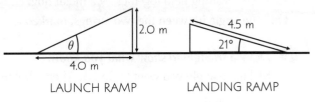

θ

2.0 m

4.0 m

LAUNCH RAMP

4.5 m

21°

LANDING RAMP

So that's right-angled triangles — what about wrong-angled triangles...

It's really helpful if you draw yourself a diagram for these kinds of questions, and that you label all the sides. This'll show you where the hypotenuse and the opposite and adjacent sides are, and help you figure out which rule to use.

The Sine and Cosine Rules

It's probably a good idea to make sure you're comfy with pages 34-39 before you get cracking on this stuff...

Some Triangles *Don't* Have a *Right-Angle*

If you're given a triangle that doesn't have a right-angle in it, and you need to find a missing side or angle, you **can't** use the standard SOH CAH TOA rules on pages 36-39.

However, there are a few things you **can** do:

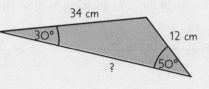

In some cases, you can **split** the triangle into **two right-angled triangles**, then use Pythagoras and the SOH CAH TOA rules.

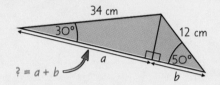

This stuff might come up in vector questions (see p.42-45).

However, if you don't know the sizes of certain sides or angles, you might not be able to find what you need by splitting the triangle up. In cases like this, you can either do a **scale drawing** and measure the missing side or angle with a ruler or a protractor (see page 43), or use the **sine** and **cosine** rules.

Use the *Sine* and *Cosine Rules* to find Missing *Lengths* and *Angles*

These are the **sine** and **cosine rules**:

The cosine rule: $\quad a^2 = b^2 + c^2 - 2bc \cos A$

If you only know one angle, call it A, and call the side opposite it a.

The sine rule: $\quad \dfrac{a}{\sin A} = \dfrac{b}{\sin B} = \dfrac{c}{\sin C}$

You can also write this as: $\dfrac{\sin A}{a} = \dfrac{\sin B}{b} = \dfrac{\sin C}{c}$

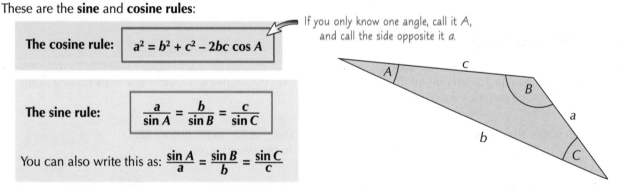

Be careful about how you **label** the sides and angles in your triangle — **capital** letters are **angles**, **lower case** letters are **sides**. Sides are labelled with the same letter as their **opposite angle** (see the triangle above).

Worked Example

Force boards are used to investigate balancing forces. A setup of one is shown on the right — three sets of masses are hung from force meters, which in turn are attached to pieces of string held together by a metal ring.

Find the angle between the two strings, marked A.

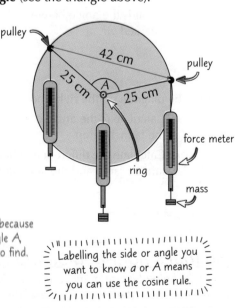

1. **Draw a triangle to show what you know.**

   Make the angle you want to find A. Then label the sides a, b and c.

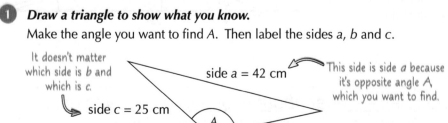

It doesn't matter which side is *b* and which is *c*.

side c = 25 cm

side a = 42 cm

This side is side *a* because it's opposite angle A, which you want to find.

side b = 25 cm

Labelling the side or angle you want to know a or A means you can use the cosine rule.

The Sine and Cosine Rules

2 **Figure out which rule to use.**

You know all of the lengths, and you're trying to find an angle, so you need to use the cosine rule.

$$a^2 = b^2 + c^2 - 2bc \cos A$$

3 **Rearrange the equation.**

$$a^2 = b^2 + c^2 - 2bc \cos A$$

↓ Add $2bc \cos A$ to both sides.

$$2bc \cos A + a^2 = b^2 + c^2$$

↓ Subtract a^2 from both sides.

$$2bc \cos A = b^2 + c^2 - a^2$$

Divide both sides by $2bc$.

$$\cos A = \frac{b^2 + c^2 - a^2}{2bc}$$

Take $\cos^{-1}$ of both sides.

$$A = \cos^{-1}\left(\frac{b^2 + c^2 - a^2}{2bc}\right)$$

If you're confident about rearranging equations, you may not need as many steps as this, but it's best to go slowly if you're not sure.

Remember, $\cos^{-1}$ is the inverse of cos.

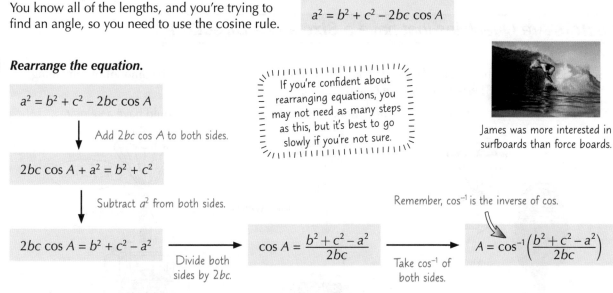

James was more interested in surfboards than force boards.

4 **Substitute in the values of a, b and c to find the answer.**

$$A = \cos^{-1}\left(\frac{25^2 + 25^2 - 42^2}{2 \times 25 \times 25}\right) = \cos^{-1}(-0.4112) = 114.28...$$

The angle marked $A = 110°$ (to 2 s.f.)

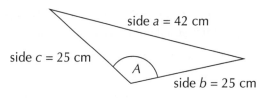
side a = 42 cm
side c = 25 cm
A
side b = 25 cm

Check the diagram in step 1 to remind yourself which side is a, which is b and which is c.

Practice Questions

Q1 The force board in the worked example above is adjusted so that the angle marked A is now 49°. What is the new distance between the two pulleys, a?

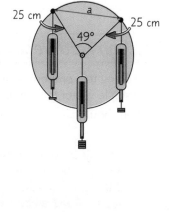
25 cm — a — 25 cm — 49°

Q2 A cyclist is at point P. He rides due north to point Q, then rides 3.9 km on a bearing of 050° to point R, before finally riding 5.8 km back to point P. The diagram on the right shows this journey.
a) Find θ_1, the angle between the lines PQ and QR.
b) Find θ_2, the angle between the lines PQ and PR.

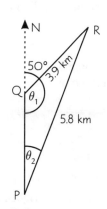
N, R, 50°, 3.9 km, Q, θ_1, 5.8 km, θ_2, P

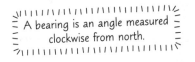
A bearing is an angle measured clockwise from north.

I can't think of any more triangle jokes — maybe it's a sine...

These two rules might look a bit confusing, but it's often quicker to use them than to draw scale drawings. Make sure you label your triangles correctly — remember, sides are named with the same letter as the angle opposite them. And if you're using the cosine rule, pick which side you call 'a' carefully — it should be opposite the angle you know (or want to find).

Vectors

The stuff on these pages relies pretty heavily on the triangle geometry covered on pages 35-41, so if you don't know your SOHs from your CAHs and your TOAs, best to have a quick flip back before you tackle this topic.

Vectors Are Quantities that have a Size and a Direction

Some quantities just have a **size**, but don't have a direction — they just tell you the **amount** of something, like mass or energy. These quantities are called **scalars**.

Other quantities have both a **size** and a **direction**. For example, a parachutist could have a velocity...

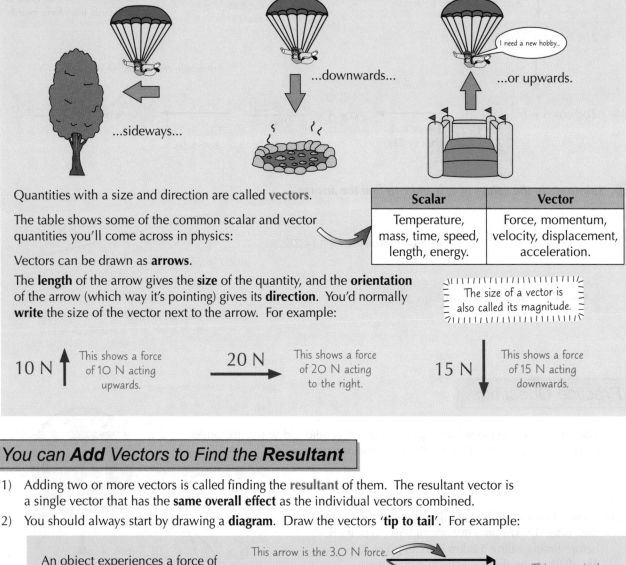

...sideways...

...downwards...

...or upwards.

I need a new hobby...

Quantities with a size and direction are called **vectors**.

The table shows some of the common scalar and vector quantities you'll come across in physics:

Vectors can be drawn as **arrows**.

The **length** of the arrow gives the **size** of the quantity, and the **orientation** of the arrow (which way it's pointing) gives its **direction**. You'd normally **write** the size of the vector next to the arrow. For example:

Scalar	Vector
Temperature, mass, time, speed, length, energy.	Force, momentum, velocity, displacement, acceleration.

The size of a vector is also called its magnitude.

10 N ↑ This shows a force of 10 N acting upwards.

20 N → This shows a force of 20 N acting to the right.

15 N ↓ This shows a force of 15 N acting downwards.

You can Add Vectors to Find the Resultant

1) Adding two or more vectors is called finding the **resultant** of them. The resultant vector is a single vector that has the **same overall effect** as the individual vectors combined.

2) You should always start by drawing a **diagram**. Draw the vectors '**tip to tail**'. For example:

An object experiences a force of 3.0 N to the right and a force of 2.0 N downwards.

This arrow is the 3.0 N force.

This arrow is the 2.0 N force. It starts where the first arrow ends.

This arrow goes from the beginning (the tail) of the first vector to the end (tip) of the second. It's the resultant force.

3) If you draw your vectors to **scale**, you can just **measure** the resultant vector from your diagram.

4) If you're combining vectors that are at **right-angles** to each other, like in the example above, you can use **Pythagoras' theorem** and **SOH CAH TOA** (see pages 36-39) to find the **magnitude** and **direction** of the resultant vector. This is usually a lot quicker and less fiddly than doing scale drawings.

If you're doing a vector subtraction, draw the vector you're subtracting with the same magnitude but pointing in the opposite direction.

5) If you're combining vectors that aren't at right angles to each other, you could also use the sine and cosine rules from pages 40-41.

Vchaptor — Vectors
Vectors

Worked Example 1

A man walks north for 500 m, then walks another 300 m on a bearing of 060°.
**By using a scale drawing, find the magnitude and direction
of his displacement at the end of his walk.**

> A bearing is just an angle measured clockwise from the north line. It is represented by three digits, e.g. 10° = 010°.

1 *Pick a sensible scale.*

The bigger your diagram, the easier it will be to draw and to take accurate measurements from — but it still needs to fit on your paper.

A good scale here is: 100 m in real life = 1 cm on the drawing.

2 *Draw a line to show the direction of north, then draw an arrow to represent the first portion of the walk.*

3 *Draw an arrow to represent the second portion of the walk.*

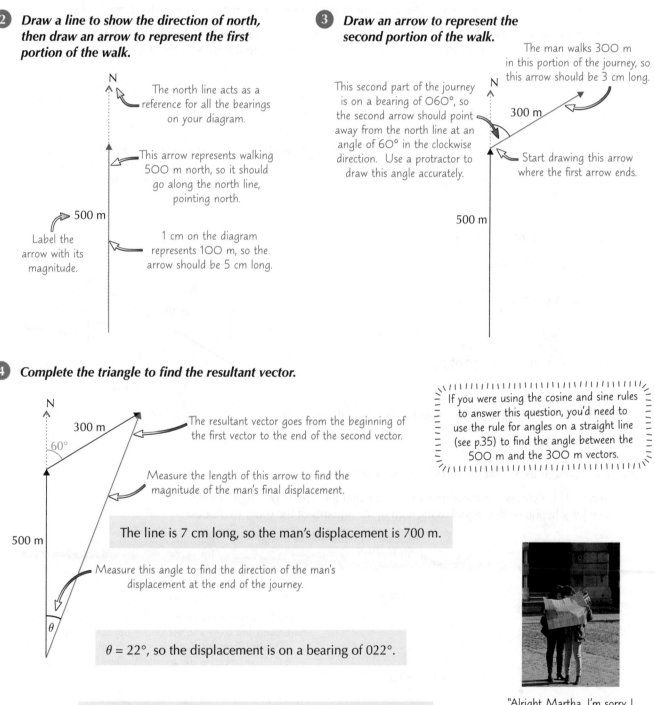

The north line acts as a reference for all the bearings on your diagram.

This arrow represents walking 500 m north, so it should go along the north line, pointing north.

Label the arrow with its magnitude.

1 cm on the diagram represents 100 m, so the arrow should be 5 cm long.

The man walks 300 m in this portion of the journey, so this arrow should be 3 cm long.

This second part of the journey is on a bearing of 060°, so the second arrow should point away from the north line at an angle of 60° in the clockwise direction. Use a protractor to draw this angle accurately.

Start drawing this arrow where the first arrow ends.

4 *Complete the triangle to find the resultant vector.*

The resultant vector goes from the beginning of the first vector to the end of the second vector.

Measure the length of this arrow to find the magnitude of the man's final displacement.

> If you were using the cosine and sine rules to answer this question, you'd need to use the rule for angles on a straight line (see p.35) to find the angle between the 500 m and the 300 m vectors.

The line is 7 cm long, so the man's displacement is 700 m.

Measure this angle to find the direction of the man's displacement at the end of the journey.

$\theta = 22°$, so the displacement is on a bearing of 022°.

The man's final displacement is 700 m on a bearing of 022°.

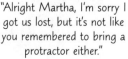

"Alright Martha, I'm sorry I got us lost, but it's not like you remembered to bring a protractor either."

Vectors

Worked Example 2

A river is flowing at a velocity of 3.0 ms⁻¹ parallel to the river bank. A ferry needs to travel across the river to a dock directly opposite its starting point, as shown on the right. The driving force provided by the ferry's engines produces a velocity of 3.4 ms⁻¹.

a) Find the angle to the current it needs to steer at to cross to the dock.

b) Find the magnitude of the resultant velocity of the ferry.

1 *Draw a diagram to show what's going on.*

The current of the river will carry the ferry downstream if it tries to steer straight across, so the ferry needs to steer into the current to give a resultant velocity straight across the river.

The resultant velocity of the ferry = the velocity of the ferry from its engines + the velocity of the river.

Draw tip-to-tail vectors showing the velocity of the river and the velocity of the ferry from its engines. Join the tip of the first vector to the tail of the second to show the resultant velocity of the ferry.

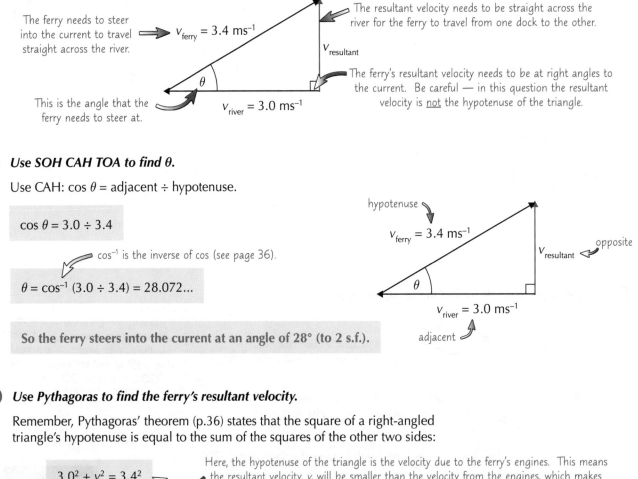

The ferry needs to steer into the current to travel straight across the river.

v_{ferry} = 3.4 ms⁻¹

The resultant velocity needs to be straight across the river for the ferry to travel from one dock to the other.

$v_{resultant}$

This is the angle that the ferry needs to steer at.

v_{river} = 3.0 ms⁻¹

The ferry's resultant velocity needs to be at right angles to the current. Be careful — in this question the resultant velocity is <u>not</u> the hypotenuse of the triangle.

2 *Use SOH CAH TOA to find θ.*

Use CAH: $\cos \theta$ = adjacent ÷ hypotenuse.

$$\cos \theta = 3.0 \div 3.4$$

$\cos^{-1}$ is the inverse of cos (see page 36).

$$\theta = \cos^{-1}(3.0 \div 3.4) = 28.072...$$

So the ferry steers into the current at an angle of 28° (to 2 s.f.).

hypotenuse

v_{ferry} = 3.4 ms⁻¹

$v_{resultant}$ opposite

v_{river} = 3.0 ms⁻¹

adjacent

3 *Use Pythagoras to find the ferry's resultant velocity.*

Remember, Pythagoras' theorem (p.36) states that the square of a right-angled triangle's hypotenuse is equal to the sum of the squares of the other two sides:

$$3.0^2 + v^2 = 3.4^2$$

Here, the hypotenuse of the triangle is the velocity due to the ferry's engines. This means the resultant velocity, v, will be <u>smaller</u> than the velocity from the engines, which makes sense — the ferry is having to 'use up' some of its velocity fighting the current.

Subtract 3.0² from both sides.

$$v^2 = 3.4^2 - 3.0^2$$

As the resultant velocity is opposite the angle θ, which you've just found, you could also use $\sin \theta$ = opposite ÷ hypotenuse, or $\tan \theta$ = opposite ÷ adjacent, but it's safest to use the numbers you're given in the question.

Take the square root of both sides.

$$v = \sqrt{3.4^2 - 3.0^2} = 1.6$$

The magnitude of the ferry's resultant velocity is 1.6 ms⁻¹.

Vectors

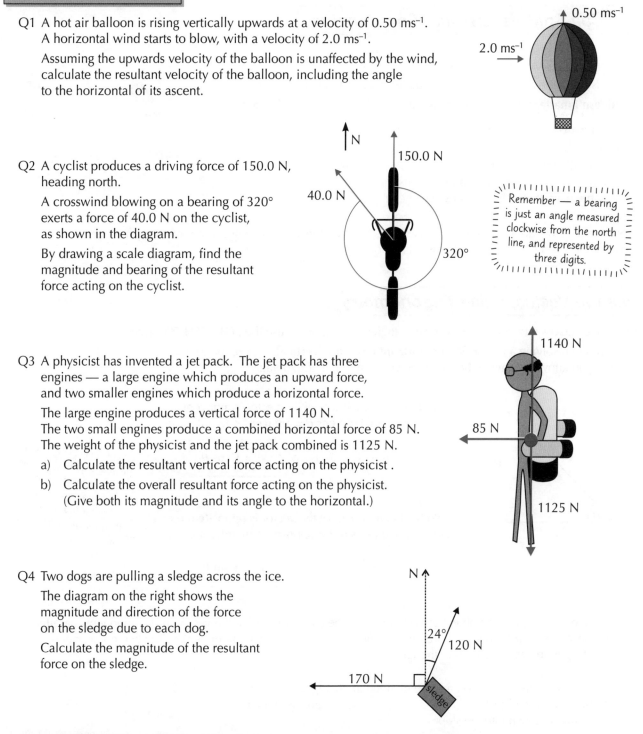

Q1 A hot air balloon is rising vertically upwards at a velocity of 0.50 ms⁻¹.
A horizontal wind starts to blow, with a velocity of 2.0 ms⁻¹.

Assuming the upwards velocity of the balloon is unaffected by the wind,
calculate the resultant velocity of the balloon, including the angle
to the horizontal of its ascent.

Q2 A cyclist produces a driving force of 150.0 N,
heading north.

A crosswind blowing on a bearing of 320°
exerts a force of 40.0 N on the cyclist,
as shown in the diagram.

By drawing a scale diagram, find the
magnitude and bearing of the resultant
force acting on the cyclist.

*Remember — a bearing
is just an angle measured
clockwise from the north
line, and represented by
three digits.*

Q3 A physicist has invented a jet pack. The jet pack has three
engines — a large engine which produces an upward force,
and two smaller engines which produce a horizontal force.

The large engine produces a vertical force of 1140 N.
The two small engines produce a combined horizontal force of 85 N.
The weight of the physicist and the jet pack combined is 1125 N.

a) Calculate the resultant vertical force acting on the physicist .

b) Calculate the overall resultant force acting on the physicist.
(Give both its magnitude and its angle to the horizontal.)

Q4 Two dogs are pulling a sledge across the ice.

The diagram on the right shows the
magnitude and direction of the force
on the sledge due to each dog.

Calculate the magnitude of the resultant
force on the sledge.

Q5 A helicopter flies south for a time, then changes course and flies 15 km on a bearing of 120°.
The magnitude of its final displacement is 26 km.

a) Calculate the bearing of the helicopter's final displacement from its start point.

b) Calculate how far the helicopter flew in the first part of its journey.

My velocity is two metres per second towards the kettle...

*You should always draw a diagram if you're answering a vector question — it makes it much easier to see what's going
on. It's generally a good idea to draw these roughly to scale, even if you're using trigonometry to find the final answer
— it'll give you an easy way to check that your calculated answer is roughly what you'd expect it to be.*

Resolving Vectors

Resolving vectors is the sort-of opposite of finding a resultant vector...

You Can **Split Vectors** into **Components**

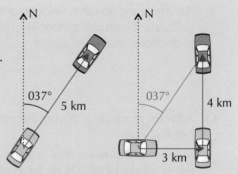

A car travels 5 km on a bearing of 037°.

This is the same as travelling 3 km to the east and 4 km to the north.

It **doesn't matter** which route the car takes, its final position is the **same**.

Splitting a vector into **components** at right angles
to each other is called **resolving** the vector.

It's basically the **opposite** of adding vectors — you're
splitting a vector up into component parts that have
the **same overall effect** as the original vector.

Splitting vectors up like this is really useful because vectors at right angles **don't affect each other**.
This means you can deal with the two directions separately.

Resolve Vectors Using **Trigonometry**

To resolve vectors into components at **right angles** to each other, use the **SOH CAH TOA** rules (p.36).

1) If you're resolving a vector (*V*) into **horizontal** (V_x) and **vertical** (V_y) components,
and you know the **angle** θ between the vector and the horizontal:

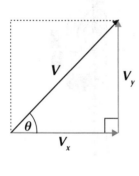

The horizontal component of the vector is **adjacent** to
the angle, so you'd use **cos θ = adjacent ÷ hypotenuse**.

$$\cos \theta = \frac{V_x}{V} \quad \text{so} \quad \boxed{V_x = V\cos\theta}$$

The vertical component of the vector is **opposite** the
angle, so you'd use **sin θ = opposite ÷ hypotenuse**.

$$\sin \theta = \frac{V_y}{V} \quad \text{so} \quad \boxed{V_y = V\sin\theta}$$

If you're given the angle from the vertical (or a bearing — an angle from a North line), then the angle from the horizontal is 90 − θ.

2) If you're working with an object on a **slope**, it can be useful to resolve the vector into components **parallel**
and **perpendicular to** the slope, (rather than horizontal and vertical components). The two components are
still at **right angles** to each other though.

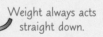
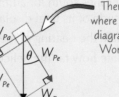

Imagine an object sitting on a slope inclined at an angle of θ to the
horizontal. The object experiences a force — its **weight, W**, which
acts straight down into the slope.

Weight always acts straight down.

In this situation, you'd want to resolve the weight
into components **parallel, W_{Pa}**, and **perpendicular, W_{Pe}**
to the slope. The component of the weight parallel to
the slope is what causes the object to slide down the slope.

There's more about where the angles in this diagram come from in Worked Example 2.

You can calculate W_{Pa} and W_{Pe} using these formulas:

$$\boxed{W_{Pa} = W\sin\theta} \quad \boxed{W_{Pe} = W\cos\theta}$$

Resolving Vectors

Worked Example 1

A footballer kicks a ball. The initial velocity of the ball is 18 ms⁻¹ at an angle of 42° above the horizontal.
Calculate the vertical and horizontal components of the ball's initial velocity.

1 **Draw a diagram to show what's going on.**
This will help you to see what you need to find.

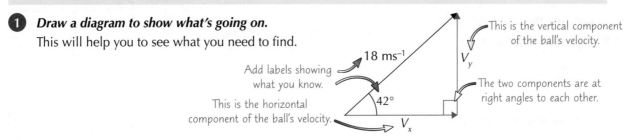

Add labels showing what you know.
This is the horizontal component of the ball's velocity.
18 ms⁻¹
42°
V_x
This is the vertical component of the ball's velocity.
V_y
The two components are at right angles to each other.

2 **Use the formulas to find the horizontal and vertical components.**

You've been given the angle to the horizontal, so you can just use the formulas on the previous page.

$$V_x = V\cos\theta = 18 \times \cos 42 = 13.376...$$

$$V_y = V\sin\theta = 18 \times \sin 42 = 12.044...$$

So the horizontal component of the ball's initial velocity is **13 ms⁻¹ (to 2 s.f.) and the vertical component of the ball's initial velocity is 12 ms⁻¹ (to 2 s.f.) upwards.**

Worked Example 2

A rollercoaster car stops partway down a slope and holds its passengers suspended for a few seconds at an angle of 40° before continuing.
The combined weight of the car and its passengers, W, is 10 000 N.
Calculate the components of W acting parallel and perpendicular to the track.

40°

1 **Draw a diagram.**
You need to resolve the force into components parallel and perpendicular to the track:

W_{Pa} is the component of the weight acting parallel to the track.

W acts straight down.

W_{Pe} is the component of the weight acting perpendicular to the track.

This is very similar to what you did in Worked Example 1 — you're just looking at components into and along the track, instead of horizontal and vertical components. Spin your book round so W_{Pa} and W_{Pe} are horizontal and vertical if that helps you to see what's going on.

2 **Add angles to your diagram.**

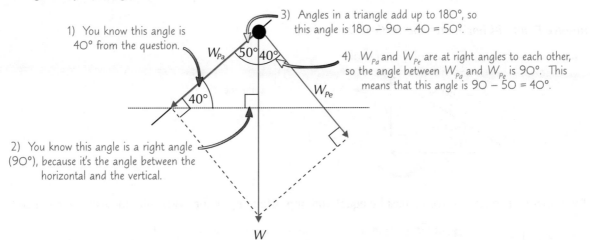

1) You know this angle is 40° from the question.

3) Angles in a triangle add up to 180°, so this angle is 180 − 90 − 40 = 50°.

4) W_{Pa} and W_{Pe} are at right angles to each other, so the angle between W_{Pa} and W_{Pe} is 90°. This means that this angle is 90 − 50 = 40°.

2) You know this angle is a right angle (90°), because it's the angle between the horizontal and the vertical.

Resolving Vectors

3 Work out W_{Pa} and W_{Pe}.

Look at the **blue triangle** in the diagram on the right. W_{Pa} and W_{Pe} are sides of this right-angled triangle. You know an angle in this triangle and the length of the hypotenuse, so you can use SOH CAH TOA.

W_{Pa} is **opposite** the angle 40°, so use:
sin θ = opposite ÷ hypotenuse:

$$\sin 40 = \frac{W_{Pa}}{W}$$

$$W_{Pa} = W \sin 40 = 10\,000 \times \sin 40 = 6427.8... \text{ N}$$

W_{Pe} is **adjacent** to the angle 40°, so use:
cos θ = adjacent ÷ hypotenuse:

$$\cos 40 = \frac{W_{Pe}}{W}$$

$$W_{Pe} = W \cos 40 = 10\,000 \times \cos 40 = 7660.4... \text{ N}$$

You could find the values of W_{Pa} and W_{Pe} from this pink triangle instead. They're exactly the same.

The method on the left is finding the lengths of these sides.

This whole shape is a rectangle, so these sides are equal to W_{Pe} and W_{Pa}.

> The component of the weight acting parallel to the track is 6000 N (to 1 s.f.) and the component of the weight acting perpendicular to the track is 8000 N (to 1 s.f.).

Worked Example 3

Three dogs are fighting over a toy. The diagram on the right shows the force exerted by each dog on the toy. The forces on the toy are balanced (so the resultant force on the toy is zero).
a) **Find the size of the angle θ.**
b) **Find the size of the missing force, F_3.**

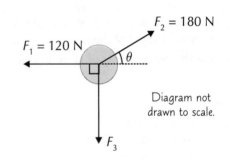

Diagram not drawn to scale.

1 Think about what you know.

Forces at right angles don't affect one another. So, if the forces on the toy are balanced, then the **horizontal components** of the forces must be balanced, and the **vertical components** of the forces must be balanced.

So: F_1 + the horizontal component of $F_2 = 0$ and F_3 + the vertical component of $F_2 = 0$

F_3 doesn't have a horizontal component, so F_2 is the only force acting against F_1.

F_1 doesn't have a vertical component, so F_2 is the only force acting against F_3.

2 Resolve F_2 into its horizontal and vertical components.

Draw a diagram to show the components of F_2.

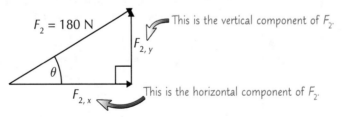

This is the vertical component of F_2.

This is the horizontal component of F_2.

The horizontal component of F_2 must be **equal and opposite** to F_1 for the horizontal forces to be balanced.

$$F_{2,x} = 120 \text{ N}$$

This is just the size of the horizontal component of F_2. The direction of this force is in the opposite direction to F_1, so the horizontal forces balance.

Resolving Vectors

 Use trigonometry to find θ.

You know the adjacent side and the hypotenuse, so use $\cos \theta = $ adjacent $\div$ hypotenuse:

$$\cos \theta = 120 \div 180 \qquad \text{So:} \qquad \theta = \cos^{-1}(120 \div 180) = 48.18...° \qquad \theta = 48° \text{ (to 2 s.f.)}$$

This is the inverse of cos (see page 36).

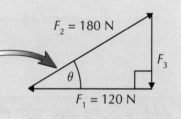

④ Use Pythagoras to find $F_{2,y}$.

You could also find $F_{2,y}$ using trigonometry and the angle you just calculated, but it's safest to use information you were given in the question:

According to Pythagoras' theorem (see p.36): $\qquad c^2 = a^2 + b^2$

So: $\quad 180^2 = 120^2 + F_{2,y}^2 \longrightarrow F_{2,y}^2 = 180^2 - 120^2 \longrightarrow F_{2,y} = \sqrt{180^2 - 120^2} = 134.16...$
$= 130 \text{ N (to 2 s.f.)}$

Remember, c is always the hypotenuse.

Subtract 120^2 from both sides.

Take the square root of both sides.

⑤ Think about the vertical forces.

From step 1, we know that the vertical component of F_2 must be **equal and opposite** to F_3 for the vertical forces to be balanced.

$$\text{So } F_3 = 130 \text{ N (to 2 s.f.)}$$

There's another way you can answer questions like this:

1) If you have **three forces** acting in the **same plane** that are in **equilibrium** (i.e. all the forces are balanced), the forces will form a **closed loop** (a triangle) if you draw them tip to tail, like this:

2) Then you can use **Pythagoras** and **trigonometry** to find any missing lengths or angles (if the triangle is right-angled) or the **sine** and **cosine rules** (if the triangle doesn't contain a right-angle — see p.36-41).

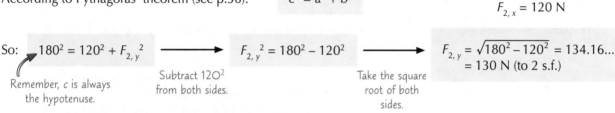

Practice Questions

Q1 A walker travels 85 km on a bearing of 035°.
 a) How far north has she travelled?
 b) How far east has she travelled?

Q2 A stuntman is fired out of a cannon, at an angle of 45° to the horizontal with a speed of 17 ms⁻¹.
 a) Calculate the vertical component of the stuntman's velocity.
 b) It takes 2.5 seconds for the stuntman to fly through the air and hit a safety net.
    What horizontal distance does he travel during this time? *(velocity = displacement ÷ time)*

Q3 A physics professor has attempted to put up a shelf in his office, but the shelf is not quite level.
 He puts a box on the shelf, and it begins to slide with an acceleration of $a = 0.85$ ms⁻² down the shelf.
 The acceleration of an object under gravity is 9.81 ms⁻² vertically downwards.
 Calculate θ, the angle of the shelf to the horizontal. You can assume that the shelf is frictionless.

Resolving vectors? But I already solved them once...

If you need to resolve a vector, make sure you pick the most sensible axes for the situation — horizontal and vertical won't always cut it. And like everything else in this section, it's really important that you draw a clear, labelled diagram.

Plotting and Reading Off Graphs

You'll be plotting a graph just about every time you do an experiment, and they're pretty much guaranteed to come up in your exams, so make sure you know the basics.

Scatter Graphs Show a **Relationship** Between **Variables**

When you carry out experiments in physics, you'll often be measuring what happens to one **variable** when another variable is changed.

For example, you might measure how the current through a component changes as the potential difference across it increases.

Potential difference / V	0.00	0.50	1.00	1.50	2.00	2.50
Current / A	0.00	0.40	0.62	0.71	0.98	0.78

It's hard to tell what's going on from a table of measurements, so you'll normally show your results in a **graph**:

This is an anomalous data point. There's more about anomalies on the next page.

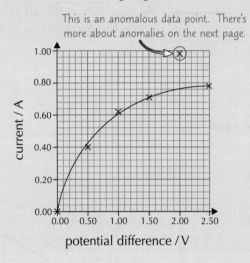

From the graph, its **really easy** to see that the current **increases** as the potential difference increases. You can also easily see that the current increases **more quickly** when the potential difference is **small** than when it's big.

Graphs like this are called **scatter graphs**. They're the graphs you're most likely to come across in physics.

This graph shows current against potential difference, not potential difference against current. It's always "the y-axis against the x-axis".

Make Sure you can **Plot** a **Scatter Graph**

1) Identify which variable is the **independent variable**, and which is the **dependent variable**.

> The **independent variable** is the thing you **change**.
> The **dependent variable** is the thing you **measure**.

A variable is any quantity that can change in an experiment.

In the example above, the potential difference is the independent variable, and the current is the dependent variable.

Generally, the **independent variable** will go **along the bottom** of your graph (the x-axis) and the **dependent variable** will go **up the side** of your graph (the y-axis).

The exception is force-extension graphs, where you'd normally plot the extension on the x-axis even though it's the dependent variable.

2) Choose **sensible scales** for your axes by looking at the **range** of your data.

> The scales you should use will depend on how much **room** you've got. You want your graph to be **easy to read**, so nice and **big**, but you also need your **scales** to be **sensible** so that you can read them easily, and plot your points without too much difficulty.

In the example above, on the x-axis, 1 division = 0.10 V, which is a nice, easy scale to work with.

On the y-axis, 5 divisions = 0.20 A, so 1 division = 0.20 ÷ 5 = 0.04 A. This is a bit trickier, but it's the kind of scale you may have to use if space is limited or a variable has an awkward range.

Plotting and Reading Off Graphs

3) **Draw** and **label** your axes, then **plot your data** with a sharp pencil.

Don't forget to include the **units** on your axes.

You should separate the units from the axis name using a **slash** (/).

Mark each data point with a **cross**.

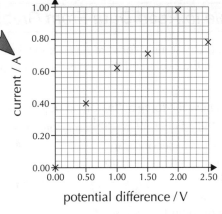

Plotting graphs was all very well and good, but Tiddles preferred plotting world domination.

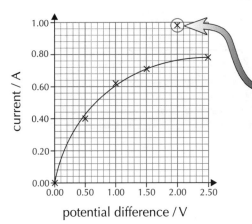

4) Draw a **line of best fit** to show the trend in your data.

You should aim to have the **same number** of points below the line as above it, with the line passing close to **as many points as possible**.

Keep an eye out for any points that **don't fit** the general trend of your data, like this one.

These are called **anomalous results**, and they are generally caused by mistakes in the experiment, like writing a variable down incorrectly.

If you've got reason to believe that a result is anomalous, you should **ignore** it when you're drawing the line of best fit.

If your line of best fit is curved, make sure that the curve is **smooth**. If it helps, try turning the paper to draw it.

> For line-graphs, e.g. a displacement-time graph for a journey, you'd join the points up rather than drawing a line of best fit. This is because there isn't a general trend, but a journey with different stages.

A *Correlation* Describes the *Relationship* Between Two *Variables*

There are three different kinds of **correlation** you need to be able to recognise:

Positive correlation:

As one variable increases the other increases. Similarly, if one variable decreases, the other variable decreases.

Negative correlation:

As one variable increases, the other decreases.

No correlation:

This means there is no relationship between the variables — there is no pattern in the data.

If you do find a correlation, you need to decide whether the effect you're seeing is **caused** by changing a variable (this is known as a **causal relationship**). There may be **another variable** that is changing **at the same time** as the independent variable and is causing the change in the dependent variable.

Plotting and Reading Off Graphs

You Need to Be Able to **Read Data** From Graphs

Reading data from graphs is pretty straight-forward if you know how to plot them. You just need to make sure you don't get the quantities on the *x*-axis and the *y*-axis mixed up, and that you **read the scales** properly.

The graph below shows how the force acting on an object varies with time. To find the force on the object after 40 seconds:

1) The time on the *x*-axis is in seconds, so find **40** on the **x-axis** and draw a line **up** to the **line of best fit**.

2) Then draw a line **across** from the line of best fit to the **y-axis** to find the force. This line meets the *y*-axis one square below 30 newtons.

3) On this axis, 5 squares = 10 newtons, so **one square** = 10 ÷ 5 = **2 newtons**. The force measurement for the red data point is 30 – 2 = **28 newtons**.

So the graph shows that, after **40 seconds**, a force of **28 newtons** acts on the object.

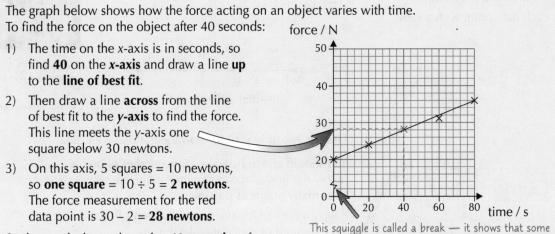

This squiggle is called a break — it shows that some values have been missed out on this axis. You can use a break to miss out a range of values on an axis that are lower than the lowest data value.

Worked Example

The data in the table on the right shows the activity of a radioactive source at different times after the start of an experiment.
Draw a graph to show how the activity of the source changes with time, and draw a line of best fit.

Time / s	0	40	80	120	160	200
Activity / Bq	150	96	76	51	30	22

The activity of a radioactive source is the number of nuclei that decay each second.

1 *Figure out which variable goes on which axis.*

You're looking at how activity changes with time, so **time** is the **independent variable** and **activity** is the **dependent variable**. That means time should go on the *x*-axis and activity should go on the *y*-axis.

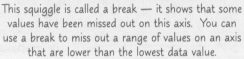

You're not exactly changing time yourself, but you're looking at the effect of time changing on activity, so time is still the independent variable.

2 *Pick sensible scales.*

You need your data to be spread out enough to see what's going on, and for the scale to be easy to use for your data.

1 square = 4 s seems like a good scale for the **time** (*x*) **axis**.
1 square = 2 Bq seems like a good scale for the **activity** (*y*) **axis**.

This means that 10 squares = 40 s. This is handy, as the time values go up in steps of 40 s.

The activity values are messier than the time values. This scale means all the plotted points will either be on a grid line or midway between two grid lines. This should make the graph fairly easy to draw without making it too big.

Make sure you're aware of how big your graph paper is when you're working out your scales — your graph will need to be somewhere between half the size of the page and the full size of the page.

Plotting and Reading Off Graphs

3 *Draw the graph.*

First draw the graph axes using the scales you've chosen.

Make sure you clearly label the axes with the correct variables and their units.

Then plot the data points using a sharp pencil.

4 *Draw a line of best fit.*

Draw a line of best fit to show the trend in your data.

These scales work well — they give you a big graph and most of the points are on grid lines rather than between them. The points all fall on major (thick) grid lines for the *x*-axis, which makes the graph much easier to draw.

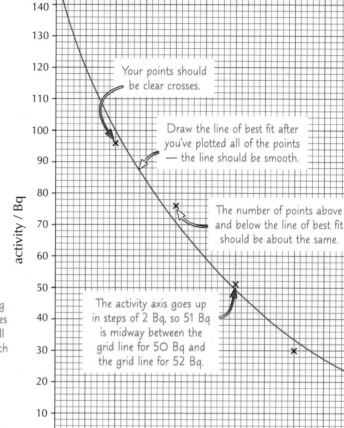

Your points should be clear crosses.

Draw the line of best fit after you've plotted all of the points — the line should be smooth.

The number of points above and below the line of best fit should be about the same.

The activity axis goes up in steps of 2 Bq, so 51 Bq is midway between the grid line for 50 Bq and the grid line for 52 Bq.

Practice Questions

Q1 The graph on the right shows how the volume of a fixed quantity of gas changes when its temperature is increased (pressure remains constant). Use the graph to find:

a) the volume of the gas when its temperature is 12 °C.

b) the temperature of the gas when its volume is 70 litres.

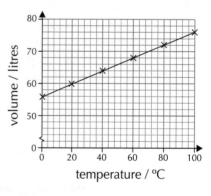

Q2 The data in the table below shows how the time taken for a ball to fall to the ground varies with the height it's dropped from.

height / m	0.10	0.20	0.30	0.40	0.50	0.60
time / s	0.14	0.20	0.25	0.21	0.32	0.35

Plot a graph of this data, and draw a line of best fit.

Warning — this section contains graphic content...

It's easy to get a bit over-confident when you're drawing graphs, so take care. If you make a mistake, anything you work out from your graph (e.g. the gradient, p.54) will also be incorrect, so take the time to make sure that you've got it right.

Linear Graphs

So you've plotted your data and drawn a line of best fit... the next step is to find the gradient and the intercept.

The **Gradient** of a **Linear Graph** is **Constant**

The **gradient** of a graph is a measure of **how steep** the line is — the steeper the line, the larger the gradient.

The gradient of a graph tells you the **rate of change** of the quantity on the **y-axis** with respect to the quantity on the x-axis (see p.56). This tells you how much of an effect a change in the x-axis variable has on the y-axis variable.

Often, the gradient of a graph will be a useful **physical quantity**. For example, the gradient of a displacement-time graph for an object's motion is equal to the velocity of the object.

When a graph is a **straight line**, its gradient is **constant**. This means you can find the gradient of the graph using any set of data points on the graph (see below).

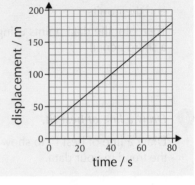

You Can Write an **Equation** for a **Straight Line**

If a line on a graph is **straight**, then the graph is **linear**. This means a change in one variable, Δx, always causes the other variable to change by a **constant multiple** of Δx. (Remember 'Δ' just means 'change in' — see page 16.)

The **line of best fit** for a linear graph has the **equation**: $\boxed{y = mx + c}$

Where **m** is the **gradient** and **c** is the y-intercept — the value of y when x = 0.

The **gradient**, *m*, is the change in the variable on the y-axis, Δy, divided by the change in the x-axis variable, Δx. This can be written as: $\boxed{m = \dfrac{\Delta y}{\Delta x}}$

If the line of best fit goes through the origin (c is 0), you can say the variables are **directly proportional** to each other: $\boxed{y \propto x}$

$\propto$ just means 'is directly proportional to' (see page 16).

Make Sure You Can **Find m** and **c** From a **Graph**

To find the gradient of a **linear** graph, you draw a triangle to find Δy and Δx:

1) Pick a **part of the line** to work with. It should start and end at points where grid lines cross — that way their x-axis and y-axis values will be easy to read off, so you'll be able to calculate the gradient as **accurately** as possible.

Here, the section of the line between 10 seconds and 30 seconds looks good.

2) Draw a **triangle**, with your section of the line as the **hypotenuse** (p.36).

3) Work out how much the **y variable changes** over the section you're looking at (Δy).

Here, $\Delta y = 140 - 60 = $ **80 m**. This is the height of your triangle.

4) Work out how much the **x variable changes** over the same section (Δx).

Here, $\Delta x = 30 - 10 = $ **20 s**. This is the base of your triangle.

5) Find $\dfrac{\Delta y}{\Delta x}$. This is the **gradient**, *m*.

Here, $m = \dfrac{\Delta y}{\Delta x} = 80 \div 20 = $ **4 ms⁻¹**.

6) The **intercept**, *c*, is just where the line meets the y-axis. Here, **c = 20 m**.

When calculating Δy you always subtract the first value from the second value.

Linear Graphs

Worked Example

A car is driving due west with a constant acceleration. The graph on the right shows the velocity of the car during a portion of the journey.

a) **Find the car's acceleration.**

b) **Find the car's initial velocity.**

c) **Write down an equation for the velocity of the car, v, in terms of time, t.**

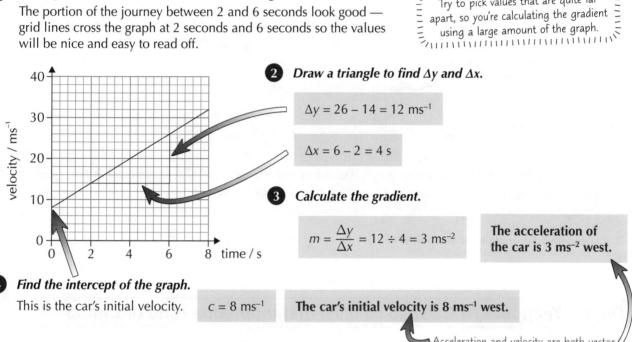

The gradient of a velocity-time graph is the acceleration.

1 *Pick a part of the line to use to calculate the gradient.*

The portion of the journey between 2 and 6 seconds look good — grid lines cross the graph at 2 seconds and 6 seconds so the values will be nice and easy to read off.

Try to pick values that are quite far apart, so you're calculating the gradient using a large amount of the graph.

2 *Draw a triangle to find Δy and Δx.*

$$\Delta y = 26 - 14 = 12 \text{ ms}^{-1}$$

$$\Delta x = 6 - 2 = 4 \text{ s}$$

3 *Calculate the gradient.*

$$m = \frac{\Delta y}{\Delta x} = 12 \div 4 = 3 \text{ ms}^{-2}$$

The acceleration of the car is 3 ms⁻² west.

4 *Find the intercept of the graph.*

This is the car's initial velocity. $c = 8 \text{ ms}^{-1}$ **The car's initial velocity is 8 ms⁻¹ west.**

Acceleration and velocity are both vector quantities (see page 42) so you need to give a direction with your answers.

5 *Write down the equation for the velocity in terms of time.*

Since the graph is linear, the equation must be in the form $y = mx + c$ (see page 54), where m is the gradient and c is the y-intercept. v is the y-axis variable and t is the x-axis variable. So, using the values calculated above for m and c, the equation for velocity is: $v = 3t + 8$

Practice Question

Q1 The graph shows the displacement of a runner during a part of a race.

Use the graph to find:

a) the runner's initial displacement.

b) the velocity of the runner during the 9 seconds shown by the graph.

Remember the gradient of a displacement-time graph is equal to the velocity.

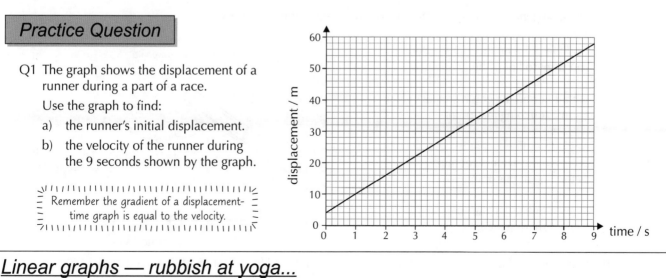

Linear graphs — rubbish at yoga...

Gradients come up all the time in physics — a lot of the time finding a quantity that's given by the gradient of a graph will be the whole point of an experiment you're doing. So make sure you're comfortable with this stuff.

Non-Linear Graphs

Finding the gradient of a curved graph is a bit trickier than finding the gradient of a straight line, but you still need to be able to do it. Make sure you're happy with pages 54-55 before you start this lot — it'll make it easier.

The **Gradient** of a **Curved Graph** Is Always **Changing**

Gradients tell you the effect of a change in the x-axis variable on the y-axis variable (see page 54).

If a graph is **curved**, a fixed change in the x-axis variable **doesn't** cause a fixed change in the y-axis variable — it varies along the curve. The **gradient** of a curved graph **changes**, it is not a constant.

This is a velocity-time graph for part of a jogger's journey:

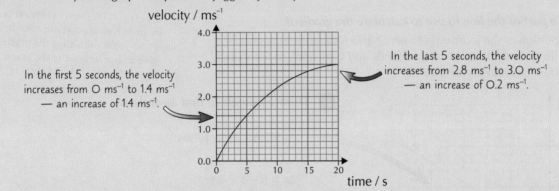

In the first 5 seconds, the velocity increases from 0 ms^{-1} to 1.4 ms^{-1} — an increase of 1.4 ms^{-1}.

In the last 5 seconds, the velocity increases from 2.8 ms^{-1} to 3.0 ms^{-1} — an increase of 0.2 ms^{-1}.

The jogger's velocity initially increases quickly, but the rate of change of velocity gets slower as time goes on.

Acceleration is the gradient of a velocity-time graph, so the graph shows the jogger's acceleration is initially high, but it falls over time.

You can find the **gradient** at any **point** on a non-linear graph like this by drawing a **tangent** to the curve.

Draw a **Tangent** to a Curve to Find the **Instantaneous Rate of Change**

1) The gradient of a curved graph is always changing. You can find the gradient at a given point, to find the **instantaneous rate of change**, by drawing a **tangent** to the curve at that point.

2) A tangent is a **straight line** that **just touches** the curve at the point you're interested in. It has the **same gradient** as the curve at that point. This means that you can find the gradient of the curve at a point by finding the gradient of its tangent.

To draw a tangent to a curve on a graph, you just need to follow these steps:

1) Find the point on the graph where you want to know the gradient.

2) Put a ruler on the graph so that it's **just touching** that point.

3) Angle the ruler so that it points in the **same direction** as the line at this point.

4) Draw a line along the ruler using a **sharp pencil**.

The ruler is pointing in the same direction as the line at this point.

The gradient of the orange line will tell you what the jogger's acceleration was after ten seconds.

Then you can just find the gradient of the tangent as you would for any straight line (see pages 54-55).

Just find the change in x (Δx) and the change in y (Δy), then find the gradient (m) using $m = \dfrac{\Delta y}{\Delta x}$.

Non-Linear Graphs

A cyclist travels south in a straight line.
The graph on the right shows the cyclist's displacement against time during a portion of the journey.
Find the cyclist's instantaneous velocity at *t* = 20 s.

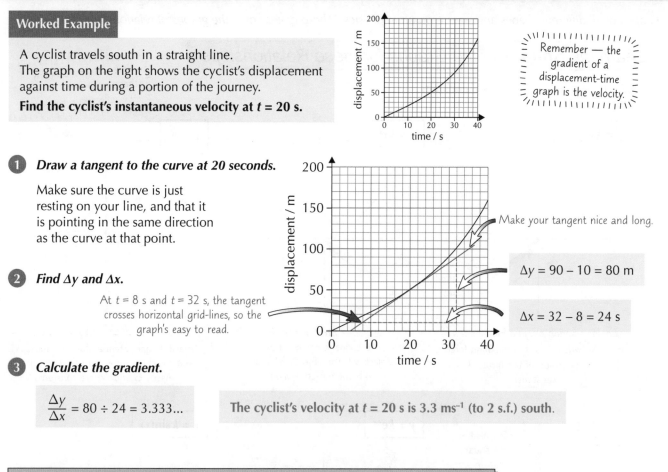

Remember — the gradient of a displacement-time graph is the velocity.

1. **Draw a tangent to the curve at 20 seconds.**

   Make sure the curve is just resting on your line, and that it is pointing in the same direction as the curve at that point.

   Make your tangent nice and long.

   $\Delta y = 90 - 10 = 80$ m

2. **Find Δy and Δx.**

   At *t* = 8 s and *t* = 32 s, the tangent crosses horizontal grid-lines, so the graph's easy to read.

   $\Delta x = 32 - 8 = 24$ s

3. **Calculate the gradient.**

   $\dfrac{\Delta y}{\Delta x} = 80 \div 24 = 3.333...$

   The cyclist's velocity at *t* = 20 s is 3.3 ms⁻¹ (to 2 s.f.) south.

You Can Find the **Average Gradient** Between Two Points

1) The **average gradient** between two points on a curve gives you the **average rate of change** for the curve over an interval.

2) It's pretty easy to find — just draw a **straight line** between the two points you're interested in, and find its gradient (see p.54).

 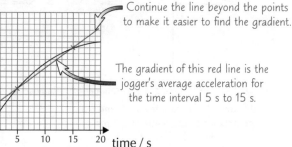

Continue the line beyond the points to make it easier to find the gradient.

The gradient of this red line is the jogger's average acceleration for the time interval 5 s to 15 s.

Q1 The acceleration of a prototype car is being tested on a straight track.
The data in the table below shows the car's velocity over time during the test.

time / s	0.0	1.0	2.0	3.0	4.0	5.0
velocity / ms⁻¹	0.0	16	22	27	28	30

a) Plot a scatter graph of this data and draw a line of best fit.

b) Use your graph to find the acceleration of the car at *t* = 3.0 s.

c) Use your graph to calculate the average acceleration of the car in the time interval 0.0 s to 3.6 s.

Remember, the gradient of a velocity-time graph is equal to the acceleration.

Curved graphs drive me round the bend...

Drawing tangents can be a real pain, but try to be patient — if you're anything like me it'll take you a few goes to get one that looks right, so work in pencil, and draw the line lightly so you can rub it out easily if you need to.

Sketching Graphs

Graphs of all different shapes and sizes crop up in physics. These pages cover the graphs of relationships you'll meet.

Learn the **Shapes** of the Graphs for these Relationships

In **all** of the graphs below, *k* is a **constant**.

If k is negative in any of these graphs, the shape will be reflected in the x-axis.

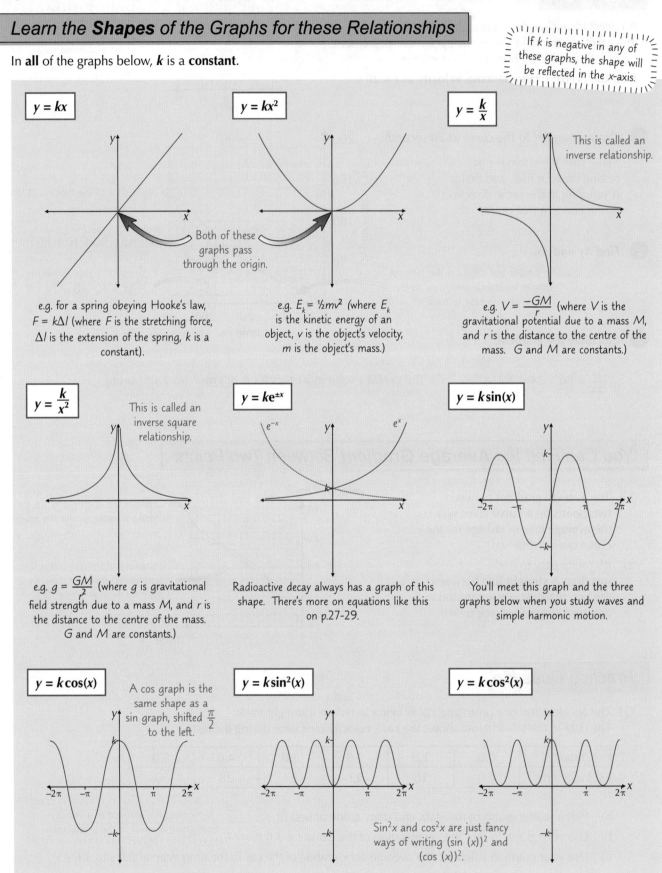

$y = kx$

$y = kx^2$

$y = \frac{k}{x}$

This is called an inverse relationship.

Both of these graphs pass through the origin.

e.g. for a spring obeying Hooke's law, $F = k\Delta l$ (where *F* is the stretching force, Δl is the extension of the spring, *k* is a constant).

e.g. $E_k = \frac{1}{2}mv^2$ (where E_k is the kinetic energy of an object, *v* is the object's velocity, *m* is the object's mass.)

e.g. $V = \frac{-GM}{r}$ (where *V* is the gravitational potential due to a mass *M*, and *r* is the distance to the centre of the mass. *G* and *M* are constants.)

$y = \frac{k}{x^2}$

This is called an inverse square relationship.

$y = ke^{\pm x}$

$y = k\sin(x)$

e^{-x} e^x

e.g. $g = \frac{GM}{r^2}$ (where *g* is gravitational field strength due to a mass *M*, and *r* is the distance to the centre of the mass. *G* and *M* are constants.)

Radioactive decay always has a graph of this shape. There's more on equations like this on p.27-29.

You'll meet this graph and the three graphs below when you study waves and simple harmonic motion.

$y = k\cos(x)$

A cos graph is the same shape as a sin graph, shifted $\frac{\pi}{2}$ to the left.

$y = k\sin^2(x)$

$y = k\cos^2(x)$

Sin^2x and cos^2x are just fancy ways of writing $(\sin(x))^2$ and $(\cos(x))^2$.

In all of these equations, '*x*' might not just be *x* — it could be multiplied by a constant, e.g. $A = A_0e^{-\lambda t}$ where λ is a constant (see page 60). The general shape of the graph (in this case *A* against *t*) will still be the same as the equivalent graph above.

SECTION THREE — GRAPH SKILLS

Sketching Graphs

Worked Example

The intensity of X-rays as they pass through a material changes with distance through the material according to the equation $I = I_0e^{-\mu x}$, where I is the intensity of the X-rays, I_0 is the initial intensity, x is the distance into the material that the X-rays have travelled, and μ is a constant.

Sketch a graph to show how I changes with x.

1 *Identify the kind of relationship you're working with.*

$I = I_0e^{-\mu x}$ is an equation of the form $y = ke^{-x}$.

2 *Draw your sketch.*

$I_0 = k$, so the intercept is at $I_{0}.$

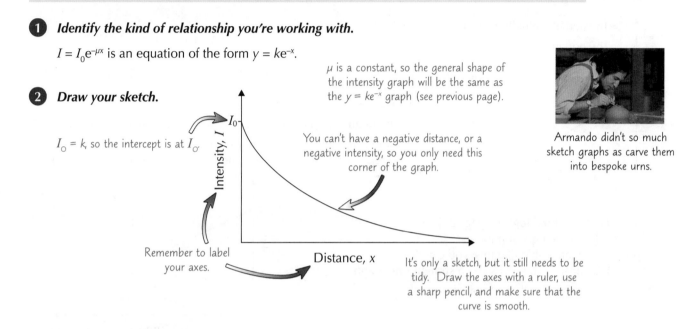

μ is a constant, so the general shape of the intensity graph will be the same as the $y = ke^{-x}$ graph (see previous page).

You can't have a negative distance, or a negative intensity, so you only need this corner of the graph.

Remember to label your axes.

It's only a sketch, but it still needs to be tidy. Draw the axes with a ruler, use a sharp pencil, and make sure that the curve is smooth.

Armando didn't so much sketch graphs as carve them into bespoke urns.

Practice Questions

Q1 Match each formula to the correct graph (A to D) below.

a) $y = kx^2$ b) $y = \dfrac{k}{x}$ c) $y = kx$ d) $y = \dfrac{k}{x^2}$

A   B   C   D

Q2 The intensity of gamma radiation falls with distance from a radioactive source according to an inverse square relationship. Sketch a graph to how the intensity of gamma radiation would vary with distance from a radioactive source.

Q3 A pendulum swings with simple harmonic motion. The displacement of this pendulum, x, is given by the equation $x = A \cos t$, where A is a constant and t is time.
The velocity of this pendulum, v, is given by the equation $v = -A \sin t$.
   a) Sketch a graph to show how the displacement of the pendulum varies with time.
   Label the x-axis and the maximum and minimum values of displacement on the y-axis.
   b) Sketch a graph to show how the velocity of the pendulum varies with time.
   Label the x-axis and the maximum and minimum values of velocity on the y-axis.

I dunno, these graphs all look a bit sketchy to me...

I'm afraid this is a case of just having to memorise a load of stuff, but it'll all be worth precious marks in your exams, so it really is worth doing. Make sure you can sketch the shapes of all the graphs on the previous page.

Logarithmic Plots

You may remember logarithms from pages 24-29. If you don't, go back and have another look at them—otherwise this is going to be a bit of an uphill struggle.

Taking **Logarithms** can Turn **Curved Graphs** into **Straight Lines**

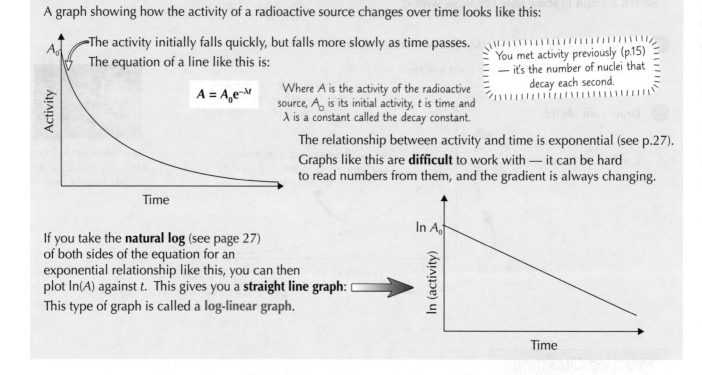

A graph showing how the activity of a radioactive source changes over time looks like this:

The activity initially falls quickly, but falls more slowly as time passes. The equation of a line like this is:

$$A = A_0 e^{-\lambda t}$$

Where A is the activity of the radioactive source, A_0 is its initial activity, t is time and λ is a constant called the decay constant.

You met activity previously (p.15) — it's the number of nuclei that decay each second.

The relationship between activity and time is exponential (see p.27). Graphs like this are **difficult** to work with — it can be hard to read numbers from them, and the gradient is always changing.

If you take the **natural log** (see page 27) of both sides of the equation for an exponential relationship like this, you can then plot ln(A) against t. This gives you a **straight line graph**: This type of graph is called a **log-linear graph**.

The **Gradient and Intercept** of a Log-Linear Graph Often Give **Useful** Values

1) Say two variables, x and z, are related by the formula $z = ke^{-ax}$ (where k and a are constants).

2) From page 28, you should know that:

$$\ln (AB) = \ln A + \ln B \qquad \ln \left(\frac{A}{B}\right) = \ln A - \ln B \qquad \ln (x^n) = n \ln x \qquad \ln (e^x) = x$$

3) So, for $z = ke^{-ax}$, if you take the natural log of both sides of the equation you get:

$$\ln z = \ln (ke^{-ax}) \implies \ln z = \ln k + \ln (e^{-ax}) \implies \ln z = \ln k - ax$$

Using the rule: $\ln (AB) = \ln A + \ln B$.   Using the rule: $\ln (e^x) = x$.

4) **$\ln z = \ln k - ax$** is in the form $y = mx + c$ — the equation of a **straight line** (see page 54). Here, $y = \ln z$, $m = -a$, and $c = \ln k$.

So, for an exponential relationship $z = ke^{-ax}$, plotting $\ln z$ against x gives a straight line graph with a **gradient** of $-a$ and a **y-intercept** of $\ln k$.

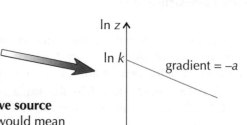

Angus had managed to give his log a fairly steep gradient.

5) This is useful if, for example, you're investigating a **radioactive source** (see the example above). Plotting a graph of $\ln(A)$ against t would mean you could find out the **values** of A_0 (the initial activity of the source) and λ (the decay constant of the source) from the y-intercept and gradient.

If you've got a relationship in the form $z = k \times 10^{-ax}$, you can take the **log base ten** of both sides of the equation instead (p.24-26). This will give you **log (z) = log (k) − ax**, which again gives you a **straight line** if you plot log (z) against x, with an **intercept** of **log (k)**, and a **gradient** of **−a**.

Logarithmic Plots

Worked Example 1

A scientist is attempting to find the decay constant, λ, for a radioactive isotope. She obtains a sample of the isotope and carries out an experiment to find out how its activity changes over time. Her results are shown in the table on the right.

By drawing a log-linear graph, find the value of λ for this isotope.

Time, t / s	Activity, A / Bq
0	98
20	75
40	72
60	52
80	38
100	33
120	30

1 *Identify the equation you're working with.*

You know from the previous page that the equation for how radioactive activity changes over time is $A = A_0e^{-\lambda t}$.

2 *Rearrange the equation to get a relationship in the form y = mx + c.*

This will give you the equation of a straight line graph that you can plot to find λ.

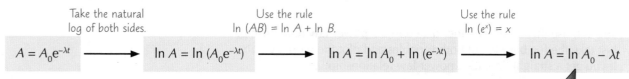

Take the natural log of both sides.   Use the rule $\ln(AB) = \ln A + \ln B$.   Use the rule $\ln(e^x) = x$

$$A = A_0e^{-\lambda t} \longrightarrow \ln A = \ln(A_0e^{-\lambda t}) \longrightarrow \ln A = \ln A_0 + \ln(e^{-\lambda t}) \longrightarrow \ln A = \ln A_0 - \lambda t$$

A_0 and λ are constants, so this equation is in the form $y = mx + c$.

Time, t / s	Activity, A / Bq	$\ln A$
0	98	$\ln 98 = 4.58$
20	75	$\ln 75 = 4.32$
40	72	$\ln 72 = 4.28$
60	52	$\ln 52 = 3.95$
80	38	$\ln 38 = 3.64$
100	33	$\ln 33 = 3.50$
120	30	$\ln 30 = 3.40$

3 *Take the natural logs of each activity value.*

The equation you found in step 2 relates $\ln A$ to time, t, so you'll need to plot $\ln A$ against t.

Redraw the table with an extra column for $\ln A$.

According to the significant figure rules for logs (p.25), you should only give these values to 2 d.p., as the activity data only has 2 significant figures.

4 *Plot a graph of $\ln A$ against t.*

Plot the points and draw a line of best fit.

5 *Find the gradient of the line.*

The equation of the line of best fit is $\ln A = \ln A_0 - \lambda t$. So the gradient of the line is equal to $-\lambda$.

See pages 54-55 if you're not sure how to find the gradient of a straight line.

$$-\lambda = \frac{\Delta y}{\Delta x} = (-1.0) \div 92 = -0.01086...$$

Give your answer to a sensible number of significant figures.

So: $\lambda = 0.01086... = \textbf{0.011 (to 2 s.f.)}$

Be careful — the gradient is equal to $-\lambda$ but you're trying to find λ, so you'll need to change the sign of your gradient.

Remember to choose sensible scales for your axes and label them correctly (see p.50).

Draw a straight line of best fit. Roughly as many points should be above the line as below it.

Pick sensible points to find the gradient from — it's easiest to read data from where the line of best fit crosses grid lines.

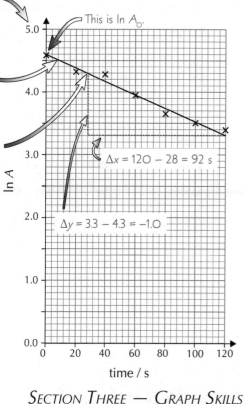

This is $\ln A_0$.

$\Delta x = 120 - 28 = 92$ s

$\Delta y = 3.3 - 4.3 = -1.0$

$\ln A$

time / s

Logarithmic Plots

You Can Use **Log-Log Graphs** to Identify **Power Law Relationships**

You can use logs to plot a straight-line graph of **any power law**.

Say the relationship between two variables x and y is $y = kx^n$.

First, take the log (base ten) of both sides of the equation:

> There's more on powers on p.23.

$$\log y = \log (kx^n)$$

Using the rule:
$\log (AB) = \log A + \log B.$

$$\log y = \log k + \log (x^n)$$

Using the rule:
$\log (x^n) = n \log x.$

$$\log y = \log k + n \log x$$

Again, this is the equation of a **straight line** — if you plotted **log y** against **log x**, you'd get a **straight line** with an **intercept** of **log k** and a **gradient** of **n**. A graph of log y against log x is called a **log-log graph**.

You can use this to **test** whether data obeys a **power law** relationship.
Just take the log base ten of both variables and plot them on a graph.
If you get a straight line, it's a power-law relationship.

Worked Example 2

An astronomer collects data on how long different planets take to orbit the Sun, and the mean radius of their orbits. His data is shown in the table on the right. The astronomer thinks the relationship between the time period and the mean radius of a planet's orbit has the form $T = kr^n$, where T is the time period, r is the mean radius, and k and n are constants.

By drawing a log-log graph, show that the astronomer is correct and find the value of n.

Planet	Mean radius of orbit, r / 1×10^6 km	Time period of orbit, T / days
Mercury	58	88
Venus	108	225
Earth	150	365
Mars	228	687
Jupiter	778	4332

1 **Calculate the log (base ten) of each planet's orbital time period and mean radius.**

Add two extra columns to the table for your calculations.

> The time period is just the time it takes for a planet to orbit the Sun once.

Planet	Mean radius of orbit, r / 1×10^6 km	$\log r$	Time period of orbit, T / days	$\log T$
Mercury	58	$\log 58 = 1.76$	88	$\log 88 = 1.94$
Venus	108	$\log 108 = 2.033$	225	$\log 225 = 2.352$
Earth	150	$\log 150 = 2.176$	365	$\log 365 = 2.562$
Mars	228	$\log 228 = 2.358$	687	$\log 687 = 2.837$
Jupiter	778	$\log 778 = 2.891$	4332	$\log 4332 = 3.6367$

If you need a reminder on the significant figure rules for logs, take a look back at page 25.

Logarithmic Plots

② *Plot a log-log graph of your results.*

Remember to draw a line of best fit.

The line of best fit is a straight line, so the astronomer was correct — the time period of a planet's orbit is related to the mean radius of the orbit in a power law relationship.

The *y* intercept is below the origin — if you need to know what it is, draw the negative part of the vertical axis and extend the line of best fit back to the *y*-axis. You don't need to worry about drawing this bit of the graph though, as you haven't been asked for it.

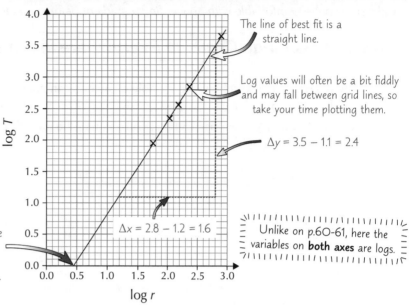

The line of best fit is a straight line.

Log values will often be a bit fiddly and may fall between grid lines, so take your time plotting them.

$\Delta y = 3.5 - 1.1 = 2.4$

$\Delta x = 2.8 - 1.2 = 1.6$

Unlike on p.60-61, here the variables on **both axes** are logs.

③ *Calculate the gradient of the line.*

Because the graph is a straight line, you know the relationship between the time period of a planet's orbit and the mean radius of its orbit has the form $T = kr^n$. This means the gradient of the line is equal to the power *n*.

$$n = \frac{\Delta y}{\Delta x} = 2.4 \div 1.6 = 1.5$$

$$n = 1.5 \text{ and } T = kr^{1.5}$$

It might seem a bit odd to have a power of $n = 1.5$, but using the index laws you met on p.23, you can see that $r^{1.5} = r^{\frac{3}{2}} = \sqrt{r^3}$. Writing out the relationship using $\sqrt{r^3}$ and rearranging shows that T^2 is proportional to r^3.

Practice Questions

Q1 The intensity of an X-ray beam is related to the distance it has travelled through a material by the equation $I = I_0 e^{-\mu x}$. I is the intensity of the X-rays (in watts per metre squared, Wm^{-2}), I_0 is the initial intensity (in Wm^{-2}), x is the distance into the material in metres, and μ is a constant relating to the material (in m^{-1}). The table below shows how the intensity of a X-ray beam varies with distance travelled through a particular material.

x / m	0.005	0.010	0.015	0.020	0.025
I / Wm^{-2}	85.4	36.5	15.6	6.7	2.9

By plotting a log-linear graph, find I_0 and μ.

Q2 The data in the table below shows how the intensity of a sound wave varies with its volume in decibels. All volumes are given to 2 s.f..

volume / dB	15	30	45	60	75	90
intensity / Wm^{-2}	3.2×10^{-11}	1.0×10^{-9}	3.2×10^{-8}	1.0×10^{-6}	3.2×10^{-5}	1.0×10^{-3}

By plotting a log-log graph, determine whether there is a power-law relationship between volume and intensity, and give a reason for your answer.

Logarithmic plots — conspiracies by forests...

The key to logarithmic plots is to make sure you're comfortable with using log rules to write exponential and power relationships in the form y = mx + c. Once you've done that, they're just like the nice linear graphs you saw on p.54.

Rates of Change

Make sure you're comfortable with how to find a gradient before you tackle this lot...

Rates of Change Come up Everywhere in Physics

A **rate of change** tells you how one variable **changes** as another variable **changes**.
Most of the ones you'll meet in your course tell you how quickly a quantity changes over **time**.

You should remember from page 54 that you can find the rate of change of a quantity over time
by plotting it on a **graph** against **time** — the rate of change at any given point is equal to the **gradient**:

You can recognise equations involving rates
of change as they'll all include a term in the form $\frac{\Delta y}{\Delta x}$:

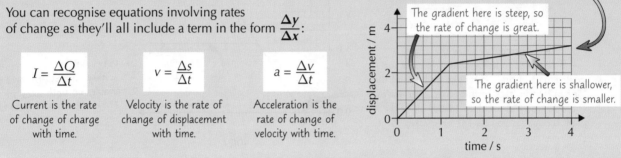

$$I = \frac{\Delta Q}{\Delta t}$$

Current is the rate
of change of charge
with time.

$$v = \frac{\Delta s}{\Delta t}$$

Velocity is the rate of
change of displacement
with time.

$$a = \frac{\Delta v}{\Delta t}$$

Acceleration is the
rate of change of
velocity with time.

The gradient here is steep, so
the rate of change is great.

The gradient here is shallower,
so the rate of change is smaller.

You can use equations involving rates of change to **model** how a quantity changes over time (p.66).

You can Find Approximate and Instantaneous Rates of Change

Normally, you'll probably see rates of change in the form $\frac{\Delta y}{\Delta x}$. In some places though, you might see
them in the form $\frac{dy}{dx}$. It can be helpful to understand how the two relate to each other mathematically:

You can find the **approximate** rate of change at a point on a
curved graph by choosing another point nearby on the curve and
drawing a **straight line** between these two points. The gradient
of this line gives you the **average rate of change** between these
two points (p.57).

Here, you're trying to find the gradient
of the curve at **ten seconds**, point **P**.
Pick another point near *P* on the curve, **Q**, and
find the **gradient** of the straight line joining them:

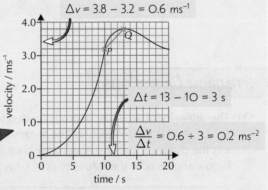

$\Delta v = 3.8 - 3.2 = 0.6 \text{ ms}^{-1}$

$\Delta t = 13 - 10 = 3 \text{ s}$

$\frac{\Delta v}{\Delta t} = 0.6 \div 3 = 0.2 \text{ ms}^{-2}$

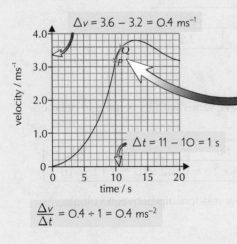

$\Delta v = 3.6 - 3.2 = 0.4 \text{ ms}^{-1}$

$\Delta t = 11 - 10 = 1 \text{ s}$

$\frac{\Delta v}{\Delta t} = 0.4 \div 1 = 0.4 \text{ ms}^{-2}$

Generally speaking, for a curved graph of *y* against *x*, the
closer the **second point** is to the point you're interested in,
the **smaller** Δy and Δx get, and the **closer** the **gradient** of the
straight line is to the actual gradient of the curve at your point.

Here, *Q* is **much closer** to *P*. The gradient of the line joining *P* and
Q is much **more similar** to the gradient of the curve at point *P*.

In general, as Δy and Δx get **smaller and smaller**, $\frac{\Delta y}{\Delta x}$ gets
closer and closer to the **instantaneous rate of change** — the
gradient you'd get if you drew a **tangent** to the curve at that
point (see p.56). We call the instantaneous rate of change $\frac{dy}{dx}$.

If a line is straight, its gradient **doesn't change** along its length.
This means, for a linear relationship, $\frac{\Delta y}{\Delta x}$ and $\frac{dy}{dx}$ are the **same**.

*In general, if a rate of change is written as $\frac{\Delta y}{\Delta t}$, this
means it's telling you the average rate of change over
the interval Δt. So for example, the equation $v = \frac{\Delta s}{\Delta t}$
tells you the average velocity over the period Δt.*

Rates of Change

Sometimes, You Need to Know the Rate of Change of a Rate of Change

Sometimes, you might be interested in how the **gradient** of a graph **changes** over time.
In cases like this, you need to find the rate of change of a rate of change:

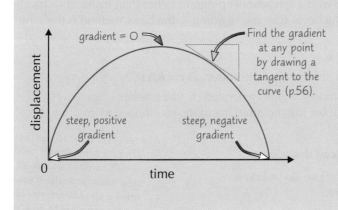

The graph on the left shows the **displacement** of an object thrown **vertically** up in the air over **time**.

The object is travelling **upwards quickly** at first, so the graph has a **steep, positive gradient**.

As the object gets higher, its **velocity decreases**, until it comes to a stop at its highest point (where the gradient is zero). It then begins to fall back towards the ground, and the gradient becomes **negative**.

As the object falls, its downwards velocity increases, so the gradient becomes **steeper**.

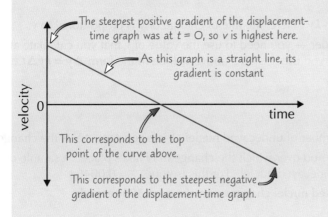

Velocity is the **rate of change of displacement**.

You can make a velocity-time graph by finding the **gradients** at **lots of points** along the displacement-time graph, plotting these against time, and drawing a **line of best fit**.

In the case of an object thrown vertically up in the air, the velocity-time graph is a **straight line**. The velocity is at its **maximum** when it's **just been thrown** (at $t = 0$), and decreases at a **steady rate**, reaching its maximum negative value as it hits the ground.

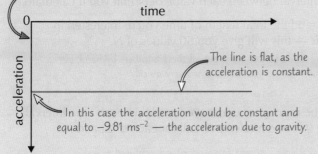

Acceleration is the **rate of change of velocity**.

This means you can make an **acceleration-time graph** by finding the **gradients** at **lots of points** along the velocity-time graph, plotting these against time, and drawing a **line of best fit**.

For an object thrown vertically up in the air, the acceleration-time graph is a **flat, straight line**. The object has a **constant acceleration** due to gravity.

Rates of Change

You can **Model** Rates of Change **Mathematically**

You can use equations involving rates of change to **model** relationships between quantities using **iteration**. In an **iterative model**, you work out how much the quantity you're interested in changes over multiple **short intervals** of time. By considering all these small steps together, you get a picture of what happens over a **larger time interval**.

It's often easier to make iterative models on a computer with a spreadsheet program rather than by hand — it's quicker and you're less likely to make mistakes. But whichever way you're doing it, the basic method is the same:

Imagine you've got an equation in the form $\frac{\Delta y}{\Delta t} = k$.

- Rearrange your equation to get Δy on its own (for the example above, $\Delta y = k\Delta t$).
- Pick a **time interval**, Δt, that the steps in your model will be separated by (the smaller the interval, the more accurate your model will be, but the more iterations you'll need to do).

Then you're ready to go:

1) **Start** at time $t = 0$, with the **initial value of** y, (call this y_0).
2) Increase the time by your time interval, Δt, and use $\Delta y = k\Delta t$ to find Δy — the **change in** y over this time interval.
3) **Add** this value of Δy to your current value of y to get the value of y after Δt. Call this new value y_1 (or y_2 or y_3 etc. depending on how many iterations you've gone through). Then go back to step 2 and **repeat the process**.

Each go round this loop is one iteration.

If you're doing this by hand, you'll have to calculate all these values yourself. If you're using a spreadsheet, you can get the computer to do a lot of the work for you — see the worked example below.

You can also use this method with equations like $\frac{\Delta y}{\Delta t} = -ky$. Here, the rate of change of y is proportional to y. Equations where y comes up twice like this are a bit harder — you need to use the value of y that you calculate at each step to find Δy for the next step — so the equation you use in step 2 above will be in the form $\Delta y = ky\Delta t$.

Worked Example

For a radioactive isotope, $\frac{\Delta N}{\Delta t} = -\lambda N$, where N is the number of undecayed nuclei, λ is a constant, ΔN is the change in the number of undecayed nuclei, and Δt is the time period over which the change in N takes place. A sample of a particular radioactive isotope initially contains 55 000 undecayed nuclei. For this isotope, $\lambda = 0.0046$ s⁻¹.

Using a spreadsheet, model how the number of undecayed nuclei changes over the next 300 seconds.

1 **Rearrange the equation to get ΔN on its own.**

You're interested in how N changes, so ΔN needs to be on its own.

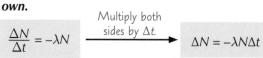

$$\frac{\Delta N}{\Delta t} = -\lambda N \xrightarrow{\text{Multiply both sides by } \Delta t.} \Delta N = -\lambda N\Delta t$$

2 **Decide on a time interval.**

You need to pick an interval of Δt — this is the time interval between each value of N that you'll calculate.

The best value to use will depend on your value of λ, and the total length of time you're interested in (300 seconds here). In this case, 5 seconds seems fair — this will give you 60 values of N.

You'd use a bigger interval if you had to work out all these numbers by hand, but the computer will do your calculations very quickly.

3 **Set up your spreadsheet.**

You'll need columns for total time (t), the change in the number of undecayed nuclei in each time interval (ΔN) and the number of undecayed nuclei remaining (N), and a reference cell for each of Δt and λ.

Label your columns so you don't get confused.

λ / s⁻¹	0.0046
Δt / s	5

t / s	ΔN	N

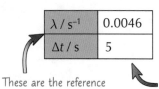

These are the reference cells for Δt and λ.

Generally, you'll need a column for each of the variables that change in the equation you're modelling (and a column for total time), and a reference cell for each of the variables that don't change.

Rates of Change

4 *Enter your formulas into your spreadsheet.*

Use $\Delta N = -\lambda N \Delta t$ to calculate the number of undecayed nuclei left in the sample after each time interval.

This column tells you the total time.

This column tells you how much N changes by in each interval Δt.

This column tells you the number of undecayed nuclei remaining at time t.

λ / s^{-1}	0.0046
Δt / s	5

Be careful when you refer to these in your formulas — make sure the cell references don't change when you autofill in new rows (iterations).

t / s	ΔN	N
$t_0 = 0$		$N_0 = 55\ 000$
$t_1 = t_0 + \Delta t$	$(\Delta N)_1 = -\lambda \times N_0 \times \Delta t$	$N_1 = N_0 + (\Delta N)_1$
$t_2 = t_1 + \Delta t$	$(\Delta N)_2 = -\lambda \times N_1 \times \Delta t$	$N_2 = N_1 + (\Delta N)_2$
$t_3 = ...$	$(\Delta N)_3 = ...$	$N_3 = ...$

If you write the formulas in each column properly, the spreadsheet can automatically fill them in for as many rows (iterations) as you want.

These are the values you should get in the first 4 rows of your spreadsheet:

t / s	ΔN	N
0		55 000
5	−1265	53 735
10	−1235.9...	52 499.0...
15	−1207.4...	51 291.6...
...	...	...

This is (−0.0046) × 55 000 × 5

This is (−0.0046) × 53 735 × 5

These numbers are all negative, as N is falling as the isotope decays.

This is 55 000 − 1265.

This is 53 735 − 1235.9....

If you're doing this by hand, you'll need to use a calculator to find the values in each row. Make sure you write down all the numbers your calculator displays for each value, so you don't get any rounding errors.

If you find spreadsheet modelling hard, have a go at setting up the spreadsheet in this example and see if you can get the same numbers.

5 *Plot a graph of your results.*

It's pretty hard to see what's going on over 60 rows of data, so it's best to plot a graph to show what's happening. Your spreadsheet software will be able to draw this for you. Your graph should look like this:

This graph shows exponential decay (see page 27).

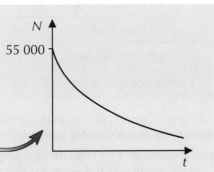

Practice Question

Q1 Capacitors are devices that store charge. When a capacitor is discharged through a resistor, the charge on it falls over time according to the equation: $\dfrac{\Delta Q}{\Delta t} = -\dfrac{Q}{RC}$. Q is the charge remaining on the capacitor at a given time, ΔQ is the change in the charge remaining on the capacitor, Δt is the time period over which the change in Q takes place, and R and C are constants.

A capacitor initially holds 5.0×10^{-3} C of charge.
At $t = 0$, the capacitor is connected to a circuit and begins to discharge. $RC = 0.50$ s.

Using an iterative spreadsheet model, and time intervals of 0.005 s, calculate the charge remaining on the capacitor after 0.03 seconds.

Rates of change — how quickly you get dressed in the morning...

This lot can seem pretty intimidating, but it's all based on ideas that you have met before. The trickiest thing here is probably figuring out how to model equations with a spreadsheet. Just take it slowly, and make sure that your columns are labelled clearly before you start, so you can keep track of what's going on.

Areas Under Graphs

As well as being able to find the gradients of lines, you need to be able to find the areas underneath them...

The **Area Under A Graph** Often **Corresponds** to a **Physical Quantity**

The **area under a graph** is the space between the **line** and the **x-axis**.
For lots of the graphs you'll meet in your course, it represents a useful **physical quantity**.

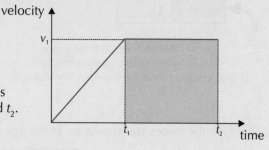

This is a graph of **velocity** against **time** for a moving object:

The area under a velocity-time graph is equal to **displacement** — for example, the area shaded blue here is equal to the change in displacement between times t_1 and t_2.

If you've got a graph made up of straight lines, then you can calculate the area under the graph (see p. 69).
If your graph is curved, then you'll have to **estimate** the area under it.

You Need to Know **Which Graphs** Have **Useful Areas**

There are quite a few situations where you might need to find the area under a graph. These include:

Graph	Area under graph
Velocity-time	Change in displacement
Acceleration-time	Change in velocity
Force-time	Impulse
Force-displacement	Work done
Charge-potential difference	Energy stored by a capacitor

For **some** of these situations, the quantity given by the area under the graph is equal to the **x-axis variable** multiplied by the **y-axis variable**.

For example, the area under a **velocity-time graph** is change in displacement which is equal to velocity × change in time:

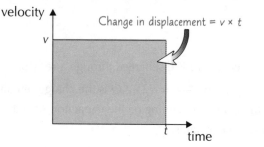

The area under a giraffe is approximately 2.5 m^2.

However, the area under a **charge-potential difference** graph for a capacitor is equal to the energy stored by the capacitor, which is $\frac{1}{2} \times Q \times V$.

Be careful — the area under a graph of y against x is **not always** $x \times y$. Just because the variables on the axes multiply to give you a quantity you're interested in, it **doesn't** necessarily mean that quantity is equal to the area under the graph. You'll be told what the area under certain graphs represent during your course, so just **learn them**.

Areas Under Graphs

You Can *Calculate* the Area Under a Graph Made Up of *Straight Lines*

If a graph is made up of **straight lines**, like the one on the right, you can calculate the area under it by breaking the area into **simple shapes**, finding the area of each shape then **adding** the areas up.

You need to make sure you look at the **scales** of your graph to find the **dimensions** of each shape.

For example, if you were trying to calculate the change in displacement between 0 and 20 seconds by finding the area under the velocity-time graph above, you could divide it into shapes like this:

The area of this triangle is:
½ × base × height = ½ × 10 × 1 = 5 m

The area of this rectangle is:
base × height = 5 × 1 = 5 m

The area of this triangle is:
½ × base × height = ½ × 5 × –1 = –2.5 m

> There's more on finding the areas of simple shapes on page 32.

> You're after the area between the line and the x-axis. If the line goes below the x-axis, then the area of that portion of the graph will be negative.

The total area under the graph is (–2.5) + 5 + 5 = **7.5 m**

You Can Estimate the Area Under a *Curved* Graph by *Counting Squares*...

If a graph is curved, then you'll only be able to **estimate** the area under it.

The simplest way of estimating the area under a curved graph is to just **count up** the **number of squares** between the **x-axis** and the **line**. Match up any **partly included** squares — for example, two squares that are half covered makes one whole included square. They don't have to match exactly, just as long as they roughly add up to one whole square.

Then **multiply** the number of squares by the quantity represented by the area of **one square** (you'll need to figure this out).

> This is the simplest method to understand, but it's a bit fiddly, so be careful.

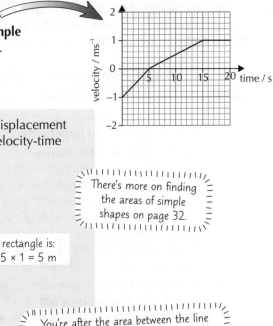

These two squares match up to create one square in the blue area.

For example, to find an estimate of the impulse between 0 and 5 seconds for the graph on the right:

1) **Count** the squares in the area you're interested in. Here, there are **12 squares** that are fully in the blue area (marked with red dots on the graph). All the squares that are partially under the graph cover a total of approximately **4 squares** in the blue area. So in total, there are **16 squares** in the blue area.

2) Look at the axes — 1 gridline on the **y-axis** represents **0.4 N**, and 1 gridline on the **x-axis** represents **1 s**. So the area of one square represents an impulse of 1 × 0.4 = **0.4 Ns**.

3) **Multiply** this quantity by the number of squares to get the impulse between 0 and 5 seconds — 0.4 × 16 = **6.4 Ns**.

Adding up all the parts of the squares that are partially in the blue area is approximately equal to three squares.

Areas Under Graphs

...Or by Breaking the Area into *Trapeziums*

You can approximate the area under the curve as a set of **trapeziums** (see page 32).
Then you just need to find the area of each trapezium, then add them up to get the total area.
The **more closely** the trapeziums follow the curve, the **better** your estimate will be.

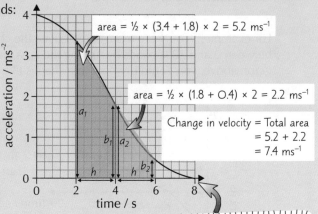

This graph shows the acceleration of a motorbike against time.

To find the change in velocity between 2 and 6 seconds:

1) Divide the area under the graph between 2 and 6 seconds into **trapeziums**.

   You need to pick a sensible **number** of trapeziums — they generally need to be **narrow enough** that they follow the curve closely, but **not so narrow** that you end up working out the areas of loads of trapeziums. It also helps to pick your trapeziums so that they're a whole number of grid squares wide. Two trapeziums looks like enough here.

2) Find the **area** of each trapezium using the formula: **area = ½(a + b)h** (h is the length of the trapezium along the **x-axis**).

3) **Add your answers up** to find the total area.

area = ½ × (3.4 + 1.8) × 2 = 5.2 ms⁻¹

area = ½ × (1.8 + 0.4) × 2 = 2.2 ms⁻¹

Change in velocity = Total area
= 5.2 + 2.2
= 7.4 ms⁻¹

If the line meets the x-axis in the area you're interested in, you'll need to break the area into triangles and trapeziums — for example you'd need a triangle between 6 and 8 seconds here.

Worked Example

A parent pushes a child along in a toy car for 40 m.
A force-displacement graph for the journey is shown on the right.

By breaking the area under the graph into trapeziums, estimate the work done by the parent in moving the child and the car from 4 m to 20 m.

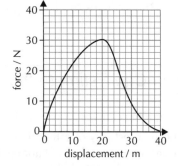

1 *Divide the area under the graph into trapeziums.*

You want to find the work done moving the child and car from 4 m to 20 m, so you need to find the area under the curve between these displacements.

It looks like 4 trapeziums, each 2 grid squares wide, will be enough.

2 *Find the area of each trapezium.*

Remember, the area of a trapezium, A = ½(a + b)h.

3 *Add up the areas.*

This will give you an estimate of the total area under the curve between 4 m and 20 m, so an estimate of the work done over this displacement.

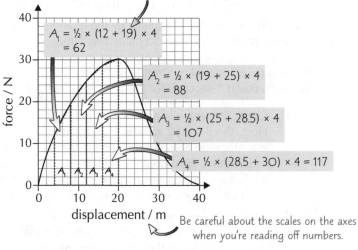

You may have to estimate values in-between grid lines. Just be as accurate as you can.

$A_1 = ½ × (12 + 19) × 4$
$= 62$

$A_2 = ½ × (19 + 25) × 4$
$= 88$

$A_3 = ½ × (25 + 28.5) × 4$
$= 107$

$A_4 = ½ × (28.5 + 30) × 4 = 117$

Be careful about the scales on the axes when you're reading off numbers.

62 + 88 + 107 + 117 = 374

Quote your final answer to a sensible number of significant figures (p.3).

The work done pushing the child from 4 m to 20 m is approximately 370 J (to 2 s.f.)

Areas Under Graphs

Practice Questions

Q1 Maya goes for a bike ride.
The graph on the right shows
her velocity against time.

Calculate the change in Maya's
displacement between 200 s and 500 s.

The area under a velocity-time graph
is equal to the change in displacement.

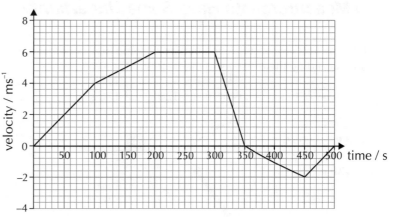

Q2 A scientist is testing the properties of a spring.

He attaches the spring to a trolley and pushes the trolley
up against a wall to squash the spring. He then releases
the trolley and measures the displacement of the trolley
and the force exerted on it by the spring.
He plots the force-displacement graph on the right.

The area under this force-displacement graph is equal
to the work done by the spring.

Estimate how much work is done on the trolley as it's
moved from 0 to 0.002 m by counting the number of
squares under the graph.

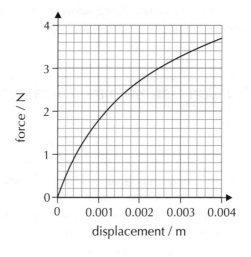

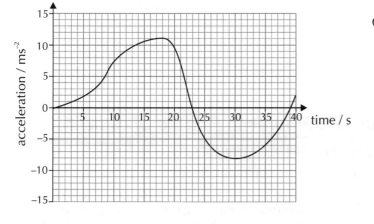

Q3 The graph on the left shows
acceleration against time for a
car during part of a journey.

The area under an acceleration-time graph
is equal to the change in velocity.

a) Using trapeziums, estimate the
change in the car's velocity between
6 seconds and 12 seconds.

b) Using trapeziums and triangles,
estimate the change in the car's
velocity between 19 seconds
and 27 seconds.

Phew, that's graphs done with — for now...

*There's a bit more coming up on pages 78-81 I'm afraid. It's really helpful for finding the areas under graphs if you
can remember the shape stuff from page 32 (particularly those tricky trapeziums). And don't forget, parts of the graph
below the x-axis have negative areas — don't let questions like 1 and 3 above catch you out.*

Uncertainties

*You can never measure anything exactly — there'll always be some **uncertainty** in your measurements.*

All Measurements Have Some Uncertainty

Imagine you're measuring the masses of some blocks with a balance and recording their masses to the nearest 10 g:

The **mass** of this block is **between 120 g** and **130 g**.

It's **closer** to **130 g**, so you'd record its mass as **130 g**.

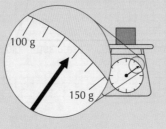

The **mass** of this block is between **130 g** and **140 g**.

Again, it's closer to **130 g**, so that's what you'd record.

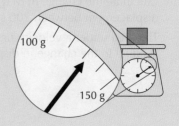

If you were told a third block had a mass of 130 g and it had been measured with this balance, you **wouldn't know** whether its actual mass was **a little bit less** than 130 g, or a **little bit more**.

We say there is some **uncertainty** in the measurement.

Uncertainties give you the **range** in which the true value of a measurement lies.

You Can **Estimate** the Uncertainty from the **Scale** on Your **Equipment**

1) Sometimes, pieces of equipment will **tell you** the uncertainty in their measurements.

2) Other times, you'll have to work it out for yourself:

> The uncertainty is generally **half the smallest division** the equipment can measure, in **either direction**.

3) The balance above has markings **every 10 g**, so 10 g is the smallest division it can measure. The uncertainty in any measurement made with this balance is **5 g** either way.

4) So the mass of the third block from the example above, given with the uncertainty in its measurement, is:

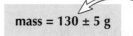

mass = 130 ± 5 g

This sign means 'plus or minus' (see p.16), so the real mass could be anywhere between 125 g and 135 g.

The maximum possible difference between your measured value and the true value (5 g here) is sometimes called the margin of error.

Uncertainties are often given with a level of confidence or probability that the true values lies in the interval they describe.

5) This kind of uncertainty is called an **absolute uncertainty**. Absolute uncertainties have the **same units** as the quantity they relate to.

You Can Use the Number of **Significant Figures** to Find the Uncertainty

If you need to find the uncertainty of a measurement and don't know anything about the equipment used to make it, you can figure out the absolute uncertainty from the number of **significant figures** (p.2-3).

> For example, the current in a circuit is given as 5.24 A. This measurement is given to three significant figures, so the **minimum value** it could have is **5.235 A** and the **maximum value** it could have is **5.245 A**. So the **uncertainty** in the current is ± **0.005 A**.

This gives you a handy general rule:

> To find the uncertainty in a measurement from the number of significant figures, take **one unit** of the last **significant figure** that the value is given to and **divide it by two**.

Uncertainties

You Can Give Uncertainties as *Fractions* or *Percentages*

Imagine you've got a voltmeter that measures potential difference (p.d.) with an uncertainty of ± 0.5 V.

> 1) If you measure a p.d. of **60 V**, the uncertainty is **quite small** compared to the size of the measurement.
>
> 2) If you measure a p.d. of **2 V**, then the uncertainty is **nearly as big** as the measurement itself.

You can turn absolute uncertainties into percentages or fractions (p.11-12) to show how the **size** of the uncertainty **compares** to the size of the measurement.

To turn an **absolute uncertainty** into a **fractional** or **percentage uncertainty**:

> 1) **Divide** the **absolute uncertainty** by the value you've **measured** to get the **fractional uncertainty**.
>
> 2) **Multiply** the fractional uncertainty by **100** to turn it into a **percentage uncertainty**.

Be careful when you write numbers with fractional uncertainties — the units go after the value, not the uncertainty. So if there's a fractional uncertainty of 0.2 in a measurement of 2.5 m, you would write 2.5 m ± 0.2.

To turn a **percentage uncertainty** back into an **absolute uncertainty**, do the opposite — **divide by 100** to get the fractional uncertainty, and then **multiply by the measured value** to turn this into the absolute uncertainty.

Some measuring devices (e.g. some ammeters) have a fixed percentage uncertainty. This means a larger measurement will have a larger absolute uncertainty.

Worked Example

The mass of a trolley is measured as 125 ± 0.5 g.
Rewrite this measurement giving the uncertainty as a percentage.

1 *Divide the absolute uncertainty by the measured value.*

0.5 ÷ 125 = 0.004 ◁— This is the fractional uncertainty.

2 *Multiply your answer by 100 to get a percentage.*

0.004 × 100 = 0.4%   So the mass of the trolley is **125 g ± 0.4%**

Graham was more interested in turning absolute uncertainties into rabbits.

Practice Questions

Q1 The display on a set of digital scales gives mass in grams to two decimal places. What is the absolute uncertainty in any measurement made using the scales?

Q2 The potential difference across a resistor is measured as 10.0 V.
    a) What is the absolute uncertainty in this measurement?
    b) What is the percentage uncertainty in this measurement?

Q3 The temperature of a gas is measured as 25.0 ± 0.05 °C. What is the fractional uncertainty in the temperature?

Q4 A ball takes 5.0 s ± 2% to roll down a slope. What is the absolute uncertainty in this measurement?

Q5 A student is trying to decide which of two ammeters to use in an experiment. Ammeter A has an uncertainty of ± 2.5% and ammeter B has an uncertainty of ± 0.05 A. The student needs to measure a current of around 1.2 A. Which ammeter should she use to minimise the absolute uncertainty in her measurement?

I'm feeling pretty uncertain about all of this to be honest...

This stuff might sound a bit horrid but it's actually quite straightforward. Just make sure you've learnt all the rules and know how to convert uncertainties between their absolute, fractional and percentage forms and you should be fine.

Combining Uncertainties

If you're working with measurements that you need to combine in some way, you need to be able to combine the uncertainties in your measurements too.

Sometimes You Need to **Combine Uncertainties**

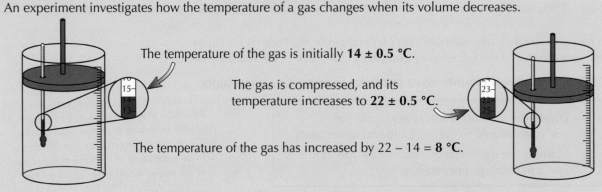

An experiment investigates how the temperature of a gas changes when its volume decreases.

The temperature of the gas is initially **14 ± 0.5 °C**.

The gas is compressed, and its temperature increases to **22 ± 0.5 °C**.

The temperature of the gas has increased by 22 – 14 = **8 °C**.

There are **two sources** of **uncertainty** in this value — the **initial temperature** and the **final temperature**. You need to know how to **combine** the two to find the uncertainty in the change in temperature.

There are **Three Rules** for **Combining Uncertainties**

> If you're **adding** or **subtracting** two or more measurements, **add** their **absolute uncertainties.**

In the example above, you're **subtracting** measurements, so you **add together** their absolute uncertainties. Both temperatures have an uncertainty of ± 0.5 °C. Adding the absolute uncertainties gives 0.5 + 0.5 = 1 so the absolute uncertainty in the change in temperature is **± 1 °C.**

This makes sense if you think about the **smallest** and **largest possible** changes in temperature:

The **largest** possible temperature change is: 22.5 – 13.5 = **9 °C**
The **smallest** possible temperature change is: 21.5 – 14.5 = **7 °C**

This is the smallest possible initial temperature and the largest possible final temperature.

The **change in temperature** is somewhere in the range 7 to 9 °C, or: **8 ± 1 °C**

> If you're **multiplying** or **dividing** measurements, **add together** their **percentage uncertainties**.

E.g. if a trolley travels a distance 5 m ± 0.1% in a time 10 s ± 0.5%, then its speed = 5 ÷ 10 = 0.5 ms⁻¹. Adding the percentage uncertainties gives 0.1 + 0.5 = 0.6, so the percentage uncertainty in the speed is **± 0.6%**.

> If you **raise a measurement to a power**, **multiply** the **percentage uncertainty** by the **power**.

E.g. if a cube has side length 10 cm ± 5%, then its volume is 10^3 = 1000 cm³. Multiplying the percentage uncertainty in the length by the power gives 5 × 3 = 15, so the percentage uncertainty in the volume is **± 15%**.

When you're giving the **absolute uncertainty** of a **calculated value**:

1) The **value shouldn't** be **more exact** than the **uncertainty** — e.g. if you calculated a value of 0.22 g, with an uncertainty of ± 0.1 g, you should **round your value** down to give 0.2 ± 0.1 g.

2) The **uncertainty shouldn't** be **more exact** than the **value** — e.g. if you calculated a value of 0.46 g, with an uncertainty of ± 0.026 g, you should **round your uncertainty** up to give 0.46 ± 0.03 g.

When you're giving a **percentage uncertainty**, you should generally give it to **one** or **two significant figures**.

Combining Uncertainties

Worked Example

When a mass is hung from a spring of length 0.35 ± 0.01 m, the spring stretches to a new length of 0.55 ± 0.01 m.
The energy stored in a stretched or compressed spring is given by the formula: $E = \frac{1}{2}k\Delta L^2$,
where E = energy (in J), k = a constant (in N m^{-1})
and ΔL = the change in the spring's length (in m).
According to the manufacturer, for this spring $k = 100$ N m^{-1} ± 10%.

a) **Calculate the change in the spring's length when the mass is hung from it.**
Give the absolute uncertainty in your answer.

b) **Calculate the energy stored in the stretched spring. Give the percentage uncertainty in your answer.**

1 *Find the change in the spring's length, ΔL.* $\Delta L = 0.55 - 0.35 = 0.20$ m

This symbol means 'change in' (p.16).   Just subtract the original length of
the spring from the extended length.

2 *Calculate the absolute uncertainty in ΔL.*

You're subtracting one measurement from another, so add the absolute uncertainties.

0.01 + 0.01 = 0.02 m   So the answer to part a) is: **0.20 ± 0.02 m**

3 *Calculate the energy stored in the spring.* $E = \frac{1}{2}k\Delta L^2 = \frac{1}{2} \times 100 \times 0.20^2 = 2$ J

4 *Convert the uncertainty in ΔL into a percentage.*

You'll need this to find the uncertainty
in the energy stored in the spring. (0.02 ÷ 0.20) × 100 = 10%

There's more about converting
between absolute and percentage
uncertainties on page 73.

5 *Calculate the uncertainty in ΔL^2.*

You're raising a measurement to a power, so
multiply the percentage uncertainty by this power. 10 × 2 = 20%

If you square a number, you're
raising it to the power of two.

6 *Calculate the uncertainty in E.*

Add together the percentage uncertainty in k and the percentage uncertainty in ΔL^2.

You've multiplied k by ΔL^2 ($E = \frac{1}{2}k\Delta L^2$). If you
multiply measurements, add the percentage uncertainties. 10 + 20 = 30%   So the answer to part b) is: **2 J ± 30%**

Practice Questions

Q1 The mass of a trolley is measured as 365 ± 0.5 g. The trolley is loaded with a mass measuring 152 ± 0.5 g.
Calculate the combined mass of the trolley and the loaded mass. Give the absolute uncertainty in your answer.

Q2 The work done by an electric current, W (in J), is given by the equation $W = VIt$, where V is the
potential difference (in V), I is the current (in A), and t is the time the current flows for (in s).
If $V = 10.0 ± 0.5$ V, $I = 2.0 ± 0.1$ A and $t = 25.0 ± 0.5$ s, calculate the work done by the current,
giving the percentage uncertainty in your answer.

Q3 A toy car with mass 0.010 ± 0.001 kg is travelling at 0.40 ± 0.01 ms^{-1}.
Calculate the car's kinetic energy and give the absolute uncertainty in your answer.
Kinetic energy (in J) = ½ × mass × velocity^2, where mass is in kg, and velocity is in ms^{-1}.

Well, you wouldn't want your uncertainties to be lonely...

When you're doing calculations, be careful that you don't mix up your percentage and absolute uncertainties.
And learn all three rules for combining uncertainties — do this and you'll go far (well...to the next page).

Calculating the Mean

When you're collecting data from an experiment, you'll normally repeat each measurement at least three times. Then you'll need to calculate a mean...

You Should Calculate a Mean of **Repeated Measurements**

If you repeatedly measured how long it took to boil a beaker of water from room temperature, you'd get a slightly different result each time:

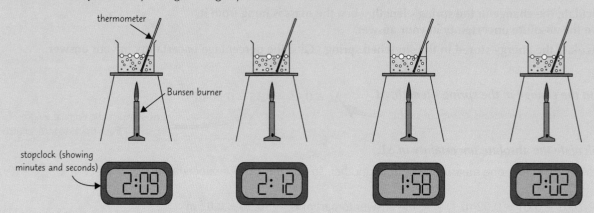

This is because, even if you're careful, there will be **small variations** in the experiment between each repeat that are **outside your control** (e.g. impurities in the water) that affect how long the water takes to boil.

Taking an **average** of repeated measurements **cancels out** some of this variation, and can help you get an answer that's closer to the true value you're interested in.

The average you need to know about in physics is the **mean**.

There's a **Simple Formula** for Calculating the Mean

You'll have come across the formula for the mean before:

$$\text{mean (average) of a measurement} = \frac{\text{sum of your repeated measurements}}{\text{number of repeats taken}}$$

Check your data for any **anomalous results** before you start (results that don't fit with the rest of the data and look like they've been caused by an error — see p.51). You shouldn't include anomalous results in your calculations.

In the example above, you'd convert the times into seconds first (so the measurements are in one unit), and then:

$$\text{mean} = \frac{129 + 132 + 118 + 122}{4} = 125.25 = \textbf{125 seconds (to 3 s.f.), or 2 minutes, 5 seconds.}$$

You Can **Estimate** the **Uncertainty** in the Mean

Estimating the **uncertainty** (p.72-73) of the mean is pretty straightforward:

1) Find the difference between your **biggest** and **smallest** recorded values (ignoring any anomalous results).
2) **Divide** this difference by two. The uncertainty is plus or minus this number.

In the example above, the shortest time is 1:58, and the longest is 2:12, so the difference between the shortest and longest time is **14 seconds**. 14 ÷ 2 = 7, so the uncertainty on the mean is **± 7 seconds**.

Calculating the Mean

Worked Example

The table below shows the results of ten repeated measurements of the count rate of a radioactive source with a long half-life. One of the results was accidentally written down incorrectly.

a) State which result was recorded incorrectly.

b) Calculate the mean count rate (in counts per minute) of the source.

c) Estimate the uncertainty in the mean.

Trial	1	2	3	4	5	6	7	8	9	10
Count rate / counts per minute	58	49	55	62	67	19	54	62	51	64

1 *Identify the anomalous result.*

Apart from trial 6, all of the count rates are in the 40s, 50s and 60s.
The result for trial 6 is at least 30 counts less than all the other results.

The result for trial 6 was recorded incorrectly.

2 *Add up the rest of the count rates, then divide by the number of trials.*

Remember, as you're not including trial 6, the total number of trials is 9, not 10.

$$\frac{58 + 49 + 55 + 62 + 67 + 54 + 62 + 51 + 64}{9} = 58$$

On average there are **58 counts per minute.**

3 *Find the difference between the lowest and highest count rates.*

The lowest count rate (excluding trial 6) is 49 counts per minute.
The highest count rate is 67 counts per minute.

$67 - 49 = 18$

4 *Divide this difference by two to get the uncertainty.*

$18 \div 2 = 9$ The uncertainty is ± **9 counts per minute.**

Practice Questions

Q1 A student is investigating the resistance of a length of wire.
She measures the wire's resistance three times, and gets values of 0.012 Ω, 0.016 Ω and 0.015 Ω.

    a) Calculate the mean resistance of the wire.

    b) Find the uncertainty in your answer to part a).

Q2 A scientist is investigating a radioactive isotope. He obtains five estimates of the isotope's half-life, shown in the table.

Estimate	1	2	3	4	5
Half-life / s	7.25×10^3	7.19×10^3	7.30×10^3	7.25×10^3	7.31×10^3

    a) Find the mean half-life of the isotope. Give the uncertainty in your answer.

    b) The scientist generates a sixth estimate of the half-life of 7.30×10^3 s. State how including this estimate would affect the value of the mean and the uncertainty in the mean.

So, if I say I make a mean stew, I'm actually saying my cooking's average...?

The mean should be familiar to you from your GCSEs, but finding the uncertainty on the mean probably isn't, so make sure you're happy with how to estimate it before you move on to the next topic.

Drawing Error Bars

It's a good idea to take a quick look at pages 50-53 if you find graphs tricky, or this lot might seem a bit like gibberish...

You Can Include *Uncertainties* on *Graphs*

A trolley is pushed along a horizontal surface. The data in the table below shows the distance of the trolley from the starting point over time. There is an **uncertainty** of ± 3 cm in the distance measurements.

Time / s	Distance / cm
2	20
4	31
6	38
8	42
10	44

If you just plot this data on a graph and draw a line of best fit (p.51) this is what you get:

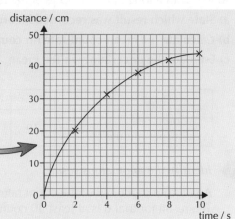

But each distance has an uncertainty of ± 3 cm, so there's a **range of possible values** each distance could actually take.

The tables below show **two possible sets of data** for how the distance might have actually varied over time:

Time / s	Distance / cm
2	23 (20 + 3)
4	34 (31 + 3)
6	35 (38 − 3)
8	39 (42 − 3)
10	41 (44 − 3)

Time / s	Distance / cm
2	17 (20 − 3)
4	28 (31 − 3)
6	41 (38 + 3)
8	45 (42 + 3)
10	47 (44 + 3)

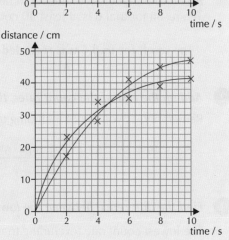

If you draw graphs of these possible sets of data with their lines of best fit, they show the same **general trend**, but they aren't quite the same — the gradient of the red line is initially very steep then decreases quickly whereas the gradient of the blue line decreases more slowly over time.

This is what **error bars** are for — they let you see the range of values your data might take.

Error Bars Show the *Uncertainty* of *Individual Points*

Error bars are just **lines** that stretch up and down (or left and right) from a data point. They tell you the **uncertainty** in that specific data point.

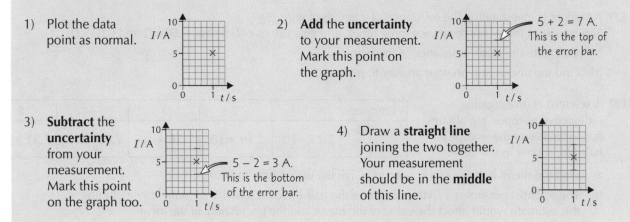

For example, a current is measured as 5 ± 2 A at t = 1 second. To plot error bars for this data point:

1) Plot the data point as normal.

2) **Add** the uncertainty to your measurement. Mark this point on the graph.

   5 + 2 = 7 A. This is the top of the error bar.

3) **Subtract** the uncertainty from your measurement. Mark this point on the graph too.

   5 − 2 = 3 A. This is the bottom of the error bar.

4) Draw a **straight line** joining the two together. Your measurement should be in the **middle** of this line.

If there's an uncertainty in the quantity plotted on the **y-axis** (as in the example here) you draw **vertical** error bars.
If there's an uncertainty in the quantity plotted on the **x-axis**, you draw **horizontal** error bars.
If there are uncertainties in **both**, you draw both **horizontal and vertical** error bars for the same data point.

Drawing Error Bars

Worked Example

The table on the right shows how the current through a resistor varies with the potential difference (p.d.) across it. The uncertainty in each of the potential difference measurements is ± 0.2 V. You can assume the uncertainty in the current measurements is negligible.

Plot these measurements on a graph, with error bars.

Potential difference / V	Current / A
2.0	0.08
4.0	0.22
6.0	0.28
8.0	0.42

1 *Calculate the maximum and minimum possible values for each measurement of potential difference.*

You might find it easier to do this in a table (especially if you need to work out absolute uncertainties from percentage uncertainties).

Potential difference / V		
measured	minimum	maximum
2.0	2.0 − 0.2 = 1.8	2.0 + 0.2 = 2.2
4.0	4.0 − 0.2 = 3.8	4.0 + 0.2 = 4.2
6.0	6.0 − 0.2 = 5.8	6.0 + 0.2 = 6.2
8.0	8.0 − 0.2 = 7.8	8.0 + 0.2 = 8.2

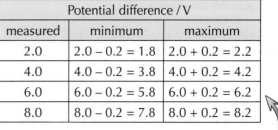

Add and subtract the uncertainty to and from each measurement of the p.d. to find the maximum and minimum possible values.

2 *Plot each data point with its error bar.*

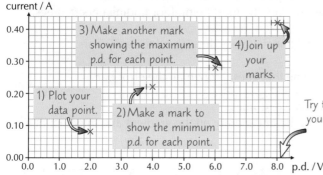

1) Plot your data point.

2) Make a mark to show the minimum p.d. for each point.

3) Make another mark showing the maximum p.d. for each point.

4) Join up your marks.

Try to pick scales for your axes that make your error bars finish on a grid line — it makes them a lot easier to draw.

The finished graph will look like this:

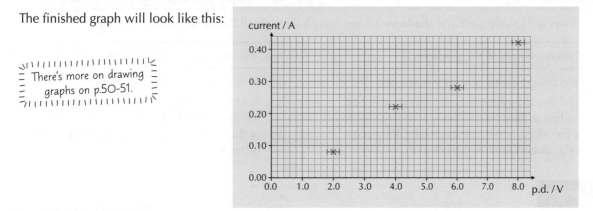

There's more on drawing graphs on p.50-51.

Practice Question

Q1 A scientist is investigating how the pressure of a gas at a fixed temperature changes with its volume.

He obtains the results shown in the table on the right. There is an uncertainty in each pressure measurement of ± 0.4 N cm^{-2}. You can assume the uncertainty in the volume measurements is negligible.

volume / m^3	0.10	0.15	0.20	0.25	0.30
pressure / N cm^{-2}	14.4	9.6	7.2	5.6	4.8

Plot a graph showing these results, including error bars.

Error bars — everyone's least favourite snack...

Error bars make graphs look a bit scary, but plotting and interpreting them is pretty straightforward once you know what's going on. Error bars come up again over the page, so learning this stuff now can only be a good thing.

Drawing Worst Lines

You can use error bars to help you work out the uncertainty on quantities that you calculate from graphs.

There Are Often **Uncertainties** in a Graph's **Gradient** and **Intercept**

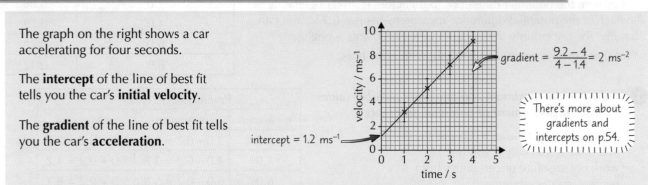

The graph on the right shows a car accelerating for four seconds.

The **intercept** of the line of best fit tells you the car's **initial velocity**.

The **gradient** of the line of best fit tells you the car's **acceleration**.

$$\text{gradient} = \frac{9.2 - 4}{4 - 1.4} = 2 \text{ ms}^{-2}$$

intercept = 1.2 ms^{-1}

There's more about gradients and intercepts on p.54.

However, this graph has **error bars**. This means there is some **uncertainty** in the **line of best fit** and therefore in the **intercept** and the **gradient** too.

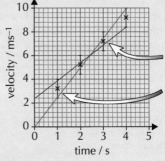

Any line that goes **through all the error bars** fits the data. The **most extreme** lines are the most helpful for finding uncertainties.

This is the **shallowest** line that goes through all the error bars.

This is the **steepest** line that goes through all the error bars.

These lines are called **worst lines**. You use them to find the uncertainty on the gradient and intercept of a graph.

Calculate the **Uncertainty** in a Gradient or Intercept Using **Worst Lines**

The worst lines are the **steepest** and **shallowest** lines that go through **all the error bars** on a graph.

To find the uncertainty in the **gradient**:

1) Find the **gradients** of your **worst lines.**
2) Find the **difference** between the gradient of the **line of best fit** and the gradients of each of the worst lines. The **greatest difference** is the **uncertainty** in the gradient.

To find the uncertainty in the **intercept**:

1) Find the **intercepts** of your **worst lines**.
2) Find the **difference** between the intercept of the **line of best fit** and the intercepts of each of the worst lines. The **greatest difference** is the **uncertainty** in the intercept.

Worked Example

The graph on the right shows the displacement of a boat against time during part of a journey.

Estimate the velocity and the initial displacement of the boat. Include the uncertainties in your answers.

The gradient of a displacement-time graph is the velocity. The intercept of a displacement-time graph is the initial displacement.

1 **Draw the line of best fit and find the gradient and intercept.**

This gives you your estimates of the boat's velocity and its initial displacement.

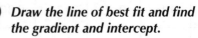

Initial displacement = 1.4 m

Velocity = 0.12 ms^{-1}

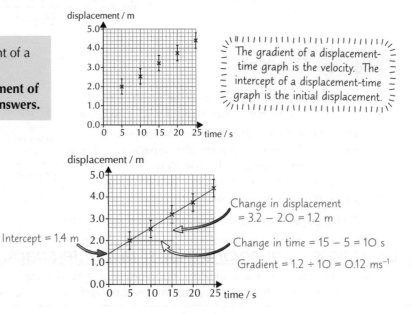

Intercept = 1.4 m

Change in displacement = 3.2 − 2.0 = 1.2 m

Change in time = 15 − 5 = 10 s

Gradient = 1.2 ÷ 10 = 0.12 ms^{-1}

Drawing Worst Lines

2 *Draw the steepest line possible that goes through all the error bars and find its gradient and intercept.*

This gives you your lowest estimate of the boat's initial displacement and your highest estimate of the boat's velocity.

Initial displacement = 0.8 m

Velocity = 0.16 ms⁻¹

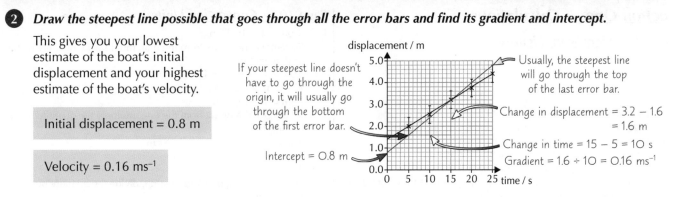

If your steepest line doesn't have to go through the origin, it will usually go through the bottom of the first error bar.

Intercept = 0.8 m

Usually, the steepest line will go through the top of the last error bar.

Change in displacement = 3.2 − 1.6 = 1.6 m

Change in time = 15 − 5 = 10 s

Gradient = 1.6 ÷ 10 = 0.16 ms⁻¹

3 *Draw the shallowest line possible that goes through all the error bars and find its gradient and intercept.*

This gives you your highest estimate of the boat's initial displacement and your lowest estimate of the boat's velocity.

Initial displacement = 2.0 m

Velocity = 0.08 ms⁻¹

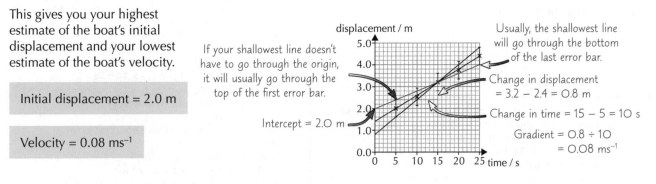

If your shallowest line doesn't have to go through the origin, it will usually go through the top of the first error bar.

Intercept = 2.0 m

Usually, the shallowest line will go through the bottom of the last error bar.

Change in displacement = 3.2 − 2.4 = 0.8 m

Change in time = 15 − 5 = 10 s

Gradient = 0.8 ÷ 10 = 0.08 ms⁻¹

4 *Find the difference between the gradient of your line of best fit and the gradient of each of your worst lines.*

The greatest difference is the uncertainty in the boat's velocity.

0.16 − 0.12 = 0.04 ms⁻¹
0.12 − 0.08 = 0.04 ms⁻¹

These differences are the same, so the uncertainty is just 0.04 ms⁻¹.

So the boat's velocity is **0.12 ± 0.04 ms⁻¹**

5 *Find the difference between the intercept of your line of best fit and the intercept of each of your worst lines.*

This gives you the uncertainty in the boat's initial displacement.

2.0 − 1.4 = 0.6 m
1.4 − 0.8 = 0.6 m

Again, these differences are the same, so the uncertainty is just 0.6 m.

So the boat's initial displacement was **1.4 ± 0.6 m**

Practice Question

Q1 The table on the right shows the extension of a spring against the force used to stretch it. Each measurement of extension has an uncertainty of ± 1 mm. Assume the uncertainty in the force is negligible. When no force is applied to the spring, its extension is zero.

a) Plot these results on a graph, with force on the *y*-axis and extension on the *x*-axis. Include error bars on your graph.

b) The gradient of a force-extension graph for a spring is called the spring constant, and is a measure of how easily a spring is stretched. Find the spring constant for this spring (in N mm⁻¹) and give the uncertainty in your answer.

force / N	extension / mm
10	5
20	10
30	15
40	20
50	25

Worst lines? I'm not a fan of the 'ten items or less' queue myself...

It's a good idea to try and find the gradients of your worst lines over a big interval — worst lines often have less tidy numbers than the line of best fit, and using a bigger interval will make your answers a bit more accurate.

Answers

Section One — Calculations

Page 3 — Significant Figures

1 a) 6
  b) 4
  c) 5
  d) 3
2 a) 1600 °C
  b) 1570 °C
  c) 1573 °C
3   speed = distance ÷ time = 522 ÷ 37 = 14.108...
    The distance is given to 3 s.f. and the speed is given to 2 s.f., so
    the answer should be given to 2 s.f. So speed = **14 ms^{-1} (to 2 s.f.)**
    If you've not seen it before, ms^{-1} is another way
    of writing m/s or metres per second.

Page 5 — Standard Form

1   0.00064 = **6.4 × 10^{-4} A**
2   1.34 × 10^5 = **134 000 s**
3   number of atoms = total mass ÷ mass of one atom
                   = 15 ÷ (6.65 × 10^{-24})
                   = 2.255... × 10^{24} = **2.3 × 10^{24} atoms (to 2 s.f.)**
4   energy = potential difference × current × time
           = 25 × (8.6 × 10^{-6}) × 650 = 0.13975 = **0.14 J (to 2 s.f.)**
5   number of years = total distance ÷ distance travelled per year
                    = (4.12 × 10^{18}) ÷ (9.5 × 10^{15})
                    = 433.684... = **430 years (to 2 s.f.)**
6   velocity = wavelength × frequency, so:
    frequency = velocity ÷ wavelength = (3.00 × 10^8) ÷ (2.4 × 10^{-9})
                    = 1.25 × 10^{17}
                    = **1.3 × 10^{17} Hz (to 2 s.f.)**

Page 7 — Units

1 a) the kelvin
  b) the kilogram
  c) the ampere
2 a) area = length × width. The S.I. unit of length is the metre,
     so the S.I. derived unit of area is m × m = **m^2**.
  b) volume = length × width × height. The S.I. unit of length is the
     metre, so the S.I. derived unit of volume is m × m × m = **m^3**.
3   S.I. unit of mass = kg
    S.I. derived unit of volume = m^3
    density = mass ÷ volume, so in S.I. base units, density is measured
    in kg ÷ m^3 = **kg m^{-3}**.
4   the Planck constant, h = wavelength × momentum
    momentum = mass × velocity, so:
    h = wavelength × (mass × velocity)
    The unit of wavelength is the metre (as it's a length),
    the unit of mass is the kilogram, and the unit of velocity is the
    metre per second.
    So, in S.I. base units, the Planck constant is measured in:
    m × (kg × ms^{-1}) = m × kg ms^{-1} = **kg m^{2}s^{-1}**

Page 10 — Converting Units

1   1 pm = 1 × 10^{-12} m
    To remove the prefix from the unit, multiply the quantity by the
    scaling factor:
    100 × (1 × 10^{-12}) = **1 × 10^{-10} m**
2   First convert from fm to m:
    1 fm = 1 × 10^{-15} m
    To remove the prefix from the unit, multiply the quantity by the
    scaling factor
    7.5 × (1 × 10^{-15}) = 7.5 × 10^{-15} m
    Then convert from m to nm:
    1 nm = 1 × 10^{-9} m
    To add a scaling prefix to the unit, divide the quantity by the
    scaling factor:
    (7.5 × 10^{-15}) ÷ (1 × 10^{-9}) = **7.5 × 10^{-6} nm**
    You could also convert directly between units. You need to multiply by
    1 × 10^{-15} and divide by 1 × 10^{-9}, so to do the conversion in one go, you'd
    just multiply the quantity by (1 × 10^{-15}) ÷ (1 × 10^{-9}) = 1 × 10^{-6}.
3   1 Gg = 1 × 10^9 g and 1 kg = 1 × 10^3 g
    To move from Gg to kg directly, you need to multiply by:
    (1 × 10^9) ÷ (1 × 10^3) = 1 × 10^6
    (7.3 × 10^{16}) × (1 × 10^6) = **7.3 × 10^{22} kg**
    Or you could convert from Gg to g (by multiplying by 1 × 10^9),
    then convert from g to kg (by dividing by 1 × 10^3).
4   1 cm = 1 × 10^{-2} m.
    So the scaling factor to move from cm^3 to m^3 is:
    (1 × 10^{-2})^3 = 1 × 10^{-6}
    Multiply by the scaling factor:
    17.3 × (1 × 10^{-6}) = **1.73 × 10^{-5} m^3**
5   1 cm = 1 × 10^{-2} m and 1 mm = 1 × 10^{-3} m.
    To move from cm to mm you need to multiply by:
    (1 × 10^{-2}) ÷ (1 × 10^{-3}) = 1 × 10^1 (or 10)
    So to move from cm^2 to mm^2 you need to multiply by:
    (1 × 10^1)^2 = 1 × 10^2
    0.0079 × (1 × 10^2) = **0.79 mm^2**
6   1 eV = 1.60 × 10^{-19} J
    To move from J to eV, divide by the scaling factor:
    (3.65 × 10^{-19}) ÷ (1.60 × 10^{-19}) = 2.281...
                    = **2.28 eV (to 3 s.f.)**
    An eV is smaller than a J, so you'd expect your answer to be larger than the
    value in the question.
7   1 kWh = 3 600 000 J
    To move from kW to J, multiply by the scaling factor:
    0.012 × (3.6 × 10^6) = 43 200 = **43 000 J (to 2 s.f.)**

Page 13 — Percentages, Fractions and Ratios

1 a) 36 ÷ 100 = 0.36
     250 × 0.36 = **90 J**
  b) Energy wasted = 250 − 45 = 205 J
     As a percentage, this is: 205 ÷ 250 = 0.82
                    0.82 × 100 = **82%**
2   $\frac{120}{375}$, divide top and bottom by 5 to give: $\frac{24}{75}$
    Then divide top and bottom by 3 to give: $\frac{8}{25}$
    The fraction could be simplified in other ways, but the final answer will be
    the same.
3 a) The total resistance of the two resistors, R_T = 12 + 4 = 16 Ω
     Write down the ratio and simplify:
     4 : 16 = **1 : 4**
  b) Write the ratio as a decimal first 1 ÷ 4 = 0.25
     The ratios of the resistances are the same as the ratios of the
     potential differences, so:
     $\frac{V_A}{V_C}$ = 0.25
     Rearrange for V_A to give:
     V_A = 0.25 × V_C = 0.25 × 8 = **2 V**

Answers

Page 15 — Probability

1   The decay constant gives the probability of a nucleus of an isotope decaying in a given second. The expected frequency of decay (the activity) is equal to this probability multiplied by the number of events (which is the number of unstable nuclei). The number of unstable nuclei in each sample is the same, so the sample with a higher decay constant will have a higher expected frequency of decay.
    5.253×10^{-8} is bigger than 3.464×10^{-11}, so the second sample will have a higher expected frequency of decay.

2   number of decays per second = decay constant × no. of nuclei
    $$= (1.05 \times 10^{-4}) \times (1.45 \times 10^{25})$$
    $$= 1.5225 \times 10^{21}$$
    $$= \mathbf{1.52 \times 10^{21}\ decays\ (to\ 3\ s.f.)}$$

3   decay constant = probability of a nucleus decaying in a second
    number of decays per second = decay constant × no. of nuclei, so
    decay constant = number of decays ÷ number of nuclei
    $$= 150 \div (3.92 \times 10^{24}) = 3.8265... \times 10^{-23}\ s^{-1}$$
    So the probability of a nucleus decaying in a given second is $\mathbf{3.8 \times 10^{-23}\ (to\ 2\ s.f.)}$.

Page 17 — Introduction to Equations

1   $\rho = m \div V = 4.5 \div 0.41 = 10.975... = \mathbf{11\ kgm^{-3}\ (to\ 2\ s.f.)}$

2   $F = \dfrac{\Delta (mv)}{\Delta t} = \dfrac{(2.0 \times 4.8) - (2.0 \times 3.5)}{8.5 - 5.0} = 0.7428...$
    $$= \mathbf{0.74\ N\ (to\ 2\ s.f.)}$$
    $\Delta (mv)$ means the change in mv, so you subtract the initial mv from the final mv.

3 a) If the wire is a cylinder, then the cross-sectional area is just the area of a circle. You need the area in m^2, so you need the radius to be in m (and therefore the diameter also needs to be in m).
    diameter of the wire = 1.2 mm = 1.2×10^{-3} m
    radius of the wire = $(1.2 \times 10^{-3}) \div 2 = 6.0 \times 10^{-4}$ m
    cross-sectional area of the wire = $\pi r^2 = \pi \times (6.0 \times 10^{-4})^2$
    $$= 1.130... \times 10^{-6}$$
    $$= \mathbf{1.1 \times 10^{-6}\ m^2\ (to\ 2\ s.f.)}$$

  b) $\rho = RA \div L = (6.7 \times 10^{-3} \times 1.130... \times 10^{-6}) \div 0.45$
    $$= 1.683... \times 10^{-8}$$
    $$= \mathbf{1.7 \times 10^{-8}\ \Omega m\ (to\ 2\ s.f.)}$$
    When you need to use a number that you calculated for an earlier part of the question, remember to use the unrounded value.

Page 21 — Working with Equations

1   $v = u + at$, subtracting u from both sides gives: $v - u = at$.

    Then divide both sides by a:

    $t = \dfrac{v - u}{a} = \dfrac{22 - 15}{0.80}$
    $$= 8.75 = \mathbf{8.8\ ms^{-2}\ (to\ 2\ s.f.)}$$
    Don't forget to give your answer to the correct number of significant figures. Here, the lowest number of significant figures given in the question is 2, so the answer must also be to 2 s.f.

2   $s = ut + \frac{1}{2}at^2$
    $s = 2.5$ m, $u = 2.0\ ms^{-1}$ and $a = -0.8\ ms^{-2}$.
    So $2.5 = 2.0t - 0.4t^2$
    which rearranges to $-0.4t^2 + 2.0t - 2.5 = 0$.
    Comparing this to the standard format for a quadratic equation, $ax^2 + bx + c = 0$, the constants are $a = -0.4$, $b = 2.0$ and $c = -2.5$.
    So $t = \dfrac{-2.0 \pm \sqrt{2.0^2 - (4 \times -0.4 \times -2.5)}}{2 \times -0.4}$
    $$= \mathbf{2.5\ s}$$
    If you tried working this out using the plus and the minus, you'll have noticed that you get the same value for both calculations. This is called a 'repeated root' or 'repeated solution' and it just means that there is only one solution.

3   $F \propto \Delta L$ so $F = k \times \Delta L$.
    Dividing both sides by ΔL gives $k = \dfrac{F}{\Delta L}$.
    First find the value of k from the first force that is applied:
    $k = \dfrac{F}{\Delta L} = 16 \div 0.025 = 640\ Nm^{-1}$
    Then rearrange $F = k \times \Delta L$ to find the new extension.
    Dividing both sides by k, gives: $\Delta L = \dfrac{F}{k}$
    So: $\Delta L = \dfrac{28}{640} = 0.04375 = \mathbf{0.044\ m\ (to\ 2\ s.f.)}$

4   $F = \dfrac{1}{4\pi\varepsilon_0} \dfrac{Q_1 Q_2}{r^2}$
    Multiplying both sides by r^2 gives: $Fr^2 = \dfrac{Q_1 Q_2}{4\pi\varepsilon_0}$.
    Dividing both sides by F gives: $r^2 = \dfrac{Q_1 Q_2}{4\pi\varepsilon_0 F}$.
    Then take the square root of both sides: $r = \sqrt{\dfrac{Q_1 Q_2}{4\pi\varepsilon_0 F}}$.
    So $r = \sqrt{\dfrac{-1.60 \times 10^{-19} \times -1.60 \times 10^{-19}}{4\pi \times 8.85 \times 10^{-12} \times 2.6 \times 10^{-11}}} = 2.975... \times 10^{-9}$
    $$= \mathbf{3.0 \times 10^{-9}\ m\ (to\ 2\ s.f.)}$$
    The square root also gives an answer of $-2.975... \times 10^{-9}$, but you can't have negative distance (it's a scalar quantity), so the positive number is the right answer.

Page 23 — Inverse Functions and Index Laws

1   Deal with the squared term first:
    $(8 \times 10^4) \div (2 \times 10^{-2})^2 = (8 \times 10^4) \div (2^2 \times (10^{-2})^2)$
    $$= (8 \times 10^4) \div (4 \times 10^{-2 \times 2})$$
    $$= (8 \times 10^4) \div (4 \times 10^{-4})$$
    Then deal with the division:
    $(8 \times 10^4) \div (4 \times 10^{-4}) = (8 \div 4) \times (10^4 \div 10^{-4})$
    $$= 2 \times 10^{4-(-4)} = \mathbf{2 \times 10^8}$$

2   $x = A\cos \omega t$ so $\cos \omega t = \dfrac{x}{A}$
    Take the inverse cos of both sides:
    $\cos^{-1}(\cos \omega t) = \cos^{-1}\left(\dfrac{x}{A}\right)$
    so $\omega t = \cos^{-1}\left(\dfrac{x}{A}\right)$ and $t = \dfrac{\cos^{-1}\left(\dfrac{x}{A}\right)}{\omega}$

    Substitute in the values from the question:
    $t = \dfrac{\cos^{-1}\left(\dfrac{0.10}{-0.15}\right)}{5.5} = \dfrac{\cos^{-1}(-0.666...)}{5.5} = 0.418... = \mathbf{0.42\ s\ (to\ 2\ s.f.)}$

Answers

Page 26 — Logarithms and Orders of Magnitude

1 a) $IL = 10\log\left(\dfrac{I}{I_0}\right)$

$I_0 = 1.0 \times 10^{-12}\,\mathrm{Wm^{-2}}$, $I = 5 \times 10^{-4}\,\mathrm{Wm^{-2}}$

$IL = 10\log(5 \times 10^{-4} \div 1.0 \times 10^{-12}) = 86.98... = \mathbf{87.0\ dB\ (to\ 1\ d.p.)}$

You should give your answer to one decimal place as $\frac{I}{I_0}$ only has one significant figure.

b) $IL = 10\log\left(\dfrac{I}{I_0}\right)$

So: $\dfrac{IL}{10} = \log\left(\dfrac{I}{I_0}\right)$

$\dfrac{IL}{10} = \log(I) - \log(I_0)$

$\dfrac{IL}{10} + \log(I_0) = \log(I)$

$\log(I) = \dfrac{67}{10} + \log(1.0 \times 10^{-12})$

$= -5.3$

Raise ten to the power of each side:

$10^{\log(I)} = 10^{-5.3}$

$I = 10^{-5.3}$

$= 5.01... \times 10^{-6} = \mathbf{5 \times 10^{-6}\ Wm^{-2}\ (to\ 1\ s.f.)}$

The power in this calculation (-5.3) only has one decimal place, so you can only give your final answer to one significant figure.

2 a) $m - M = 5\log\left(\dfrac{d}{10}\right)$ so $M = m - 5\log\left(\dfrac{d}{10}\right)$

$m = +1.60$, $d = 96$ parsecs

$M = 1.60 - (5 \times \log(96 \div 10)) = -3.311... = \mathbf{-3.3\ (to\ 2\ s.f.)}$

1.60 is to 3 s.f. and log(9.6) = 0.98 to 2 d.p. (which is correct to 2 s.f.), so you should give your answer to two significant figures.

b) $m - M = 5\log\left(\dfrac{d}{10}\right)$ so $d = 10 \times 10^{\frac{m-M}{5}}$

$M = -3.9$, $m = +1.3$

$\dfrac{m-M}{5} = (1.3 - -3.9) \div 5 = 1.04$

$d = 10 \times 10^{1.04} = 109.6.... = \mathbf{100\ parsecs\ (to\ 1\ s.f.)}$

The power in this calculation (1.04) is only accurate to 2 s.f., and therefore 1 d.p, so you should give your final answer to one significant figure.

Page 29 — Natural Logs and Exponentials

1 a) $Q = Q_0 e^{\frac{-t}{RC}}$

$Q_0 = 0.016$ C, $RC = 0.16$ s, $t = 0.02$ s

$\dfrac{-t}{RC} = -0.02 \div 0.16 = -0.125\ (= -0.1\ \text{to 1 s.f.})$

$Q = 0.016 \times e^{-0.125} = 0.01441... = \mathbf{0.01\ C\ (to\ 1\ s.f.)}$

Q_0 is given to 2 significant figures. The power in this equation (-0.125) can only be accurate to 1 s.f., so 1 d.p., so the exponential part of the equation only has one significant figure. So you can only give your answer to one significant figure.

b) $Q = Q_0(1 - e^{\frac{-t}{RC}})$

$\dfrac{-t}{RC} = -0.04 \div 0.16 = -0.25\ (= -0.3\ \text{to 1 s.f.})$

$Q = 0.016 \times (1 - e^{-0.25}) = 3.539... \times 10^{-3} = \mathbf{4 \times 10^{-3}\ C\ (to\ 1\ s.f.)}$

0.016 is given to 2 s.f., but the power -0.25 can only be given to 1 s.f., so 1 d.p., so $e^{-0.25}$ should be given to 1 s.f. So the final answer is given to 1 s.f.

2 $N = N_0 e^{-\lambda t}$

$\dfrac{N}{N_0} = e^{-\lambda t}$

$\ln\left(\dfrac{N}{N_0}\right) = \ln(e^{-\lambda t})$

$\ln\left(\dfrac{N}{N_0}\right) = -\lambda t$

$\lambda = -\dfrac{\ln\left(\dfrac{N}{N_0}\right)}{t}$

$t = 550$ s, $N_0 = 2.40 \times 10^{23}$, $N = 1.50 \times 10^{23}$

$\dfrac{N}{N_0} = (1.50 \times 10^{23}) \div (2.40 \times 10^{23}) = 0.625$

$\lambda = -\dfrac{\ln(0.625)}{550} = \dfrac{0.4700...}{550} = 8.545... \times 10^{-4}$

$= \mathbf{8.5 \times 10^{-4}\ s^{-1}\ (to\ 2\ s.f.)}$

This is a tricky one for significant figures. t is only given to 2 s.f., so your final answer shouldn't have more than 2 s.f. You're taking the natural log of a number with three significant figures, so you can only give a value of ln(0.625) to 3 d.p. ln(0.625) = 0.470 to 3 d.p., and 0.470 has three significant figures.

So, you're dividing a number you know to 3 s.f. by another number you know to 2 s.f., hence you should give your final answer to 2 s.f.

Page 31 — Estimating

1 a) E.g. A balloon has a diameter of around 10 cm when filled with water, so its radius is about 5 cm.

Volume $= \dfrac{4}{3}\pi r^3 = \dfrac{4}{3} \times \pi \times 5^3 = 523.5... \approx \mathbf{500\ cm^3}$

Estimates of the radius of the balloon up to about 10 cm are OK.

b) Water has a density of about 1 g per cm^3, so (assuming the mass of the balloon itself is negligible) the mass of the balloon when filled with water is about 500 g, or **0.5 kg**

2 1 mm is very small, so the measurement error is likely to be high. Increasing the mass by about 100 g each time will change the extension by a reasonable amount that it is outside the margins of error, and so can be measured with the ruler with mm scaling.

3 $v = \sqrt{\dfrac{2GM}{r}}$

$\dfrac{v_{\text{Earth}}}{v_{\text{Pluto}}} = \dfrac{\sqrt{\dfrac{2GM_{\text{Earth}}}{r_{\text{Earth}}}}}{\sqrt{\dfrac{2GM_{\text{Pluto}}}{r_{\text{Pluto}}}}} = \dfrac{\sqrt{\dfrac{M_{\text{Earth}}}{r_{\text{Earth}}}}}{\sqrt{\dfrac{M_{\text{Pluto}}}{r_{\text{Pluto}}}}} = \sqrt{\dfrac{M_{\text{Earth}}}{r_{\text{Earth}}}} \times \sqrt{\dfrac{r_{\text{Pluto}}}{M_{\text{Pluto}}}}$

$= \sqrt{\dfrac{M_{\text{Earth}}\, r_{\text{Pluto}}}{M_{\text{Pluto}}\, r_{\text{Earth}}}}$

$M_{\text{Earth}} \approx 500 M_{\text{Pluto}}$

$r_{\text{Earth}} \approx 5 r_{\text{Pluto}}$

Therefore: $\dfrac{v_{\text{Earth}}}{v_{\text{Pluto}}} = \sqrt{\dfrac{500 M_{\text{Pluto}}\, r_{\text{Pluto}}}{M_{\text{Pluto}}\, 5 r_{\text{Pluto}}}} = \sqrt{\dfrac{500}{5}} = \sqrt{100} = 10$

An object would need to travel roughly ten times faster to escape the gravitational field of Earth than it would need to travel to escape the gravitational field of Pluto.

Section Two — Geometry and Trigonometry

Page 33 — Area, Surface Area and Volume

1 a) For a cuboid, surface area = sum of the areas of the six rectangular sides.

2 sides are 25.0 cm by 12.0 cm. $25.0 \times 12.0 = 300\ cm^2$

2 sides are 25.0 cm by 5.0 cm. $25.0 \times 5.0 = 125\ cm^2$

2 sides are 12.0 cm by 5.0 cm. $12.0 \times 5.0 = 60\ cm^2$

surface area $= (2 \times 300) + (2 \times 125) + (2 \times 60)$

$= \mathbf{970\ cm^2}$

b) volume $= 0.250 \times 0.120 \times 0.050 = 1.5 \times 10^{-3}\ m^3$

density = mass ÷ volume, so mass = density × volume

mass $= 19\,000 \times (1.5 \times 10^{-3}) = 28.5 = \mathbf{29\ kg\ (to\ 2\ s.f.)}$

The lengths here are in cm, but the density is in $kg\,m^{-3}$, so you need to either convert the lengths into m or the density into $kg\,cm^{-3}$. It's a lot easier to convert the lengths.

2 Model the atom as a sphere:

volume $= \dfrac{4}{3}\pi r^3 = \dfrac{4}{3} \times \pi \times (1.4 \times 10^{-10})^3 = 1.149... \times 10^{-29}\ m^3$

density = mass ÷ volume $= (9.3 \times 10^{-26}) \div (1.149... \times 10^{-29})$

$= 8091.14... = \mathbf{8100\ kg\ m^{-3}\ (to\ 2\ s.f.)}$

3    $p \propto \frac{1}{V}$ so $p = \frac{k}{V}$ where k is a constant.

Model the tube as a cylinder.
Volume of a cylinder $= \pi r^2 h$. $r = 12 \div 2 = 6$ cm
Initially, $h = 25$ cm so $V = \pi \times 6^2 \times 25 = 2827.433...$ cm^3
Initially, $p = 5.2 \times 10^4$ Pa. Use these values to find k:
$p = \frac{k}{V}$ so $k = pV = (5.2 \times 10^4) \times 2827.433...$
$= 1.47... \times 10^8$ Pa cm^3
When the piston is depressed, the height of the tube decreases to $25 - 1.5 = 23.5$ cm.
The new volume of the cylinder is therefore:
$V = \pi \times 6^2 \times 23.5 = 2657.78...$ cm^3
and the pressure is $p = \frac{k}{V} = (1.47... \times 10^8) \div 2657.78...$
$= 55319.14... = \textbf{5.5} \times \textbf{10}^4 \textbf{ Pa (to 2 s.f.)}$

Questions like this can get a bit complicated, so it's a good idea to check that your answer is sensible. The volume of the tube has become smaller, so the same amount of gas occupies a smaller space, hence the pressure must have gone up. If you ended up with the pressure going down, it'd mean you'd made a mistake somewhere. If you find this working tricky, go back and have a look at p.20-21 for more on proportional relationships.

Page 35 — Working with Angles

1   Angle in degrees $= \frac{180}{\pi} \times$ angle in radians
$= \frac{180}{\pi} \times 0.20\pi = \textbf{36}°$

2   Angle in radians $= \frac{\pi}{180} \times$ angle in degrees $= \frac{\pi}{180} \times 22$
$= 0.383... = \textbf{0.38 radians (to 2 s.f.)}$

3   In a month, the Earth travels through approximately 1/12 of its orbit.
This means it travels through an angle of $2\pi \div 12 = \frac{\pi}{6}$ radians.
Arc length $= \theta r = \frac{\pi}{6} \times (1.5 \times 10^{11}) = 7.853... \times 10^{10}$
$= \textbf{7.9} \times \textbf{10}^{10} \textbf{ m (to 2 s.f.)}$

Page 39 — Pythagoras and Trigonometry

1   Start off by drawing a triangle:

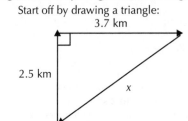

Use Pythagoras to find the missing length: $x = \sqrt{2.5^2 + 3.7^2}$
$= 4.465...$ km
Total distance $= 2.5 + 3.7 + 4.465... = 10.665...$ km
$= \textbf{11 km (to 2 s.f.)}$

2
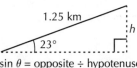

$\sin \theta = $ opposite $\div$ hypotenuse
so: opposite $=$ hypotenuse $\times \sin \theta$
$h = 1.25 \times \sin 23 = 0.488... = \textbf{0.49 km (to 2 s.f.)}$

3 a)   Call the length of the rod l.
Using Pythagoras: $55^2 = 43^2 + l^2$, so $l^2 = 55^2 - 43^2$
$l = \sqrt{55^2 - 43^2} = 34.292... = \textbf{34 cm (to 2 s.f.)}$
b)

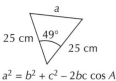

$\theta = \cos^{-1}$ (adjacent $\div$ hypotenuse) $= \cos^{-1} (43 \div 55)$
$= 38.572... = \textbf{39}° \textbf{ (to 2 s.f.)}$

4 a)

$\theta = \tan^{-1}$ (opposite $\div$ adjacent) $= \tan^{-1} (2.0 \div 4.0) = 26.565...$
$= \textbf{27}° \textbf{ (to 2 s.f.)}$

b)   First find the height, h of the landing ramp:

$\sin \theta = $ opposite $\div$ hypotenuse, so: opposite $=$ hypotenuse $\times \sin \theta$
$h = 4.5 \times \sin 21 = 1.612...$ m
Then find the difference between the heights of the two ramps:
$2.0 - 1.612... = 0.387... = \textbf{0.39 m (to 2 s.f.)}$

Page 41 — The Sine and Cosine Rules

1

$a^2 = b^2 + c^2 - 2bc \cos A$
So: $a^2 = 25^2 + 25^2 - (2 \times 25 \times 25 \times \cos 49) = 429.926...$
$a = \sqrt{429.926...} = 20.734... = \textbf{21 cm (to 2 s.f.)}$

2 a)   Angles on a straight line add up to $180°$, so $\theta_1 = 180 - 50 = \textbf{130}°$

b)   Add θ_1 to the diagram from the question:

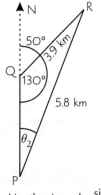

Use the sine rule: $\frac{\sin A}{a} = \frac{\sin B}{b} = \frac{\sin C}{c}$
So: $\frac{\sin 130}{5.8} = \frac{\sin \theta_2}{3.9}$
Therefore: $\sin \theta_2 = \frac{3.9 \times \sin 130}{5.8}$
and: $\theta_2 = \sin^{-1} \left(\frac{3.9 \times \sin 130}{5.8} \right) = 31.004... = \textbf{31}° \textbf{ (to 2 s.f.)}$

Answers

Page 45 — Vectors

1

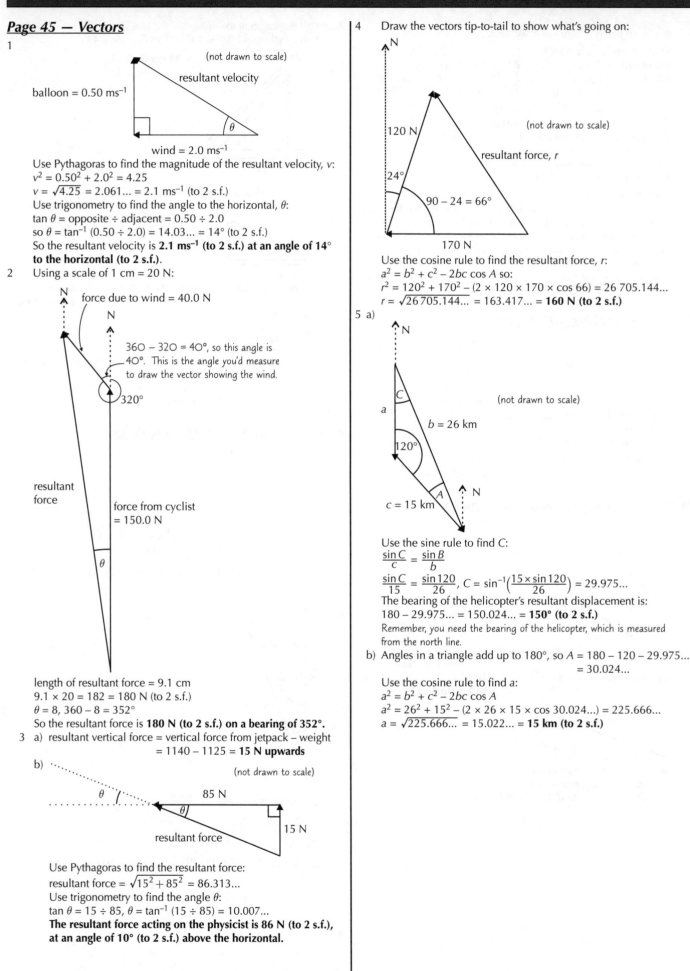

(not drawn to scale)

resultant velocity

balloon = 0.50 ms⁻¹

θ

wind = 2.0 ms⁻¹

Use Pythagoras to find the magnitude of the resultant velocity, v:
$v^2 = 0.50^2 + 2.0^2 = 4.25$
$v = \sqrt{4.25} = 2.061... = 2.1$ ms⁻¹ (to 2 s.f.)
Use trigonometry to find the angle to the horizontal, θ:
tan θ = opposite ÷ adjacent = 0.50 ÷ 2.0
so $\theta = \tan^{-1}(0.50 ÷ 2.0) = 14.03... = 14°$ (to 2 s.f.)
So the resultant velocity is **2.1 ms⁻¹ (to 2 s.f.) at an angle of 14° to the horizontal (to 2 s.f.)**.

2 Using a scale of 1 cm = 20 N:

N

force due to wind = 40.0 N

N

360 − 320 = 40°, so this angle is 40°. This is the angle you'd measure to draw the vector showing the wind.

320°

resultant force

force from cyclist = 150.0 N

θ

length of resultant force = 9.1 cm
9.1 × 20 = 182 = 180 N (to 2 s.f.)
$\theta = 8$, 360 − 8 = 352°
So the resultant force is **180 N (to 2 s.f.) on a bearing of 352°**.

3 a) resultant vertical force = vertical force from jetpack − weight
= 1140 − 1125 = **15 N upwards**

b)

(not drawn to scale)

θ

85 N

θ

15 N

resultant force

Use Pythagoras to find the resultant force:
resultant force = $\sqrt{15^2 + 85^2} = 86.313...$
Use trigonometry to find the angle θ:
tan θ = 15 ÷ 85, $\theta = \tan^{-1}(15 ÷ 85) = 10.007...$
The resultant force acting on the physicist is 86 N (to 2 s.f.), at an angle of 10° (to 2 s.f.) above the horizontal.

4 Draw the vectors tip-to-tail to show what's going on:

N

120 N

resultant force, r

(not drawn to scale)

24°

90 − 24 = 66°

170 N

Use the cosine rule to find the resultant force, r:
$a^2 = b^2 + c^2 - 2bc \cos A$ so:
$r^2 = 120^2 + 170^2 - (2 × 120 × 170 × \cos 66) = 26\,705.144...$
$r = \sqrt{26\,705.144...} = 163.417... = $ **160 N (to 2 s.f.)**

5 a)

N

a

C

$b = 26$ km

(not drawn to scale)

120°

A

N

$c = 15$ km

Use the sine rule to find C:
$\dfrac{\sin C}{c} = \dfrac{\sin B}{b}$
$\dfrac{\sin C}{15} = \dfrac{\sin 120}{26}$, $C = \sin^{-1}\left(\dfrac{15 × \sin 120}{26}\right) = 29.975...$
The bearing of the helicopter's resultant displacement is:
180 − 29.975... = 150.024... = **150° (to 2 s.f.)**
Remember, you need the bearing of the helicopter, which is measured from the north line.

b) Angles in a triangle add up to 180°, so $A = 180 - 120 - 29.975...$
= 30.024...

Use the cosine rule to find a:
$a^2 = b^2 + c^2 - 2bc \cos A$
$a^2 = 26^2 + 15^2 - (2 × 26 × 15 × \cos 30.024...) = 225.666...$
$a = \sqrt{225.666...} = 15.022... = $ **15 km (to 2 s.f.)**

Answers

Page 49 — Resolving Vectors

1 a)

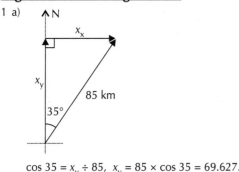

cos 35 = $x_y \div 85$, $x_y = 85 \times \cos 35 = 69.627... =$ **70 km (to 2 s.f.)**

b) sin 35 = $x_x \div 85$, $x_x = 85 \times \sin 35 = 48.753... =$ **49 km (to 2 s.f.)**

2 a) Draw a diagram:

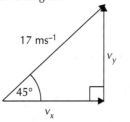

Find the vertical component of the stuntman's velocity, v_y:
$v_y = 17 \times \sin 45 = 12.020... =$ **12 ms⁻¹ (to 2 s.f.)**

b) Find the horizontal component of the stuntman's velocity, v_x:
$v_x = 17 \times \cos 45 = 12.020...$ ms⁻¹
velocity = displacement ÷ time, so:
displacement = velocity × time
= v_x × time
= 12.020... × 2.5 = 30.052... = **30 m (to 2 s.f.)**

3 Draw a sketch to show what's going on:

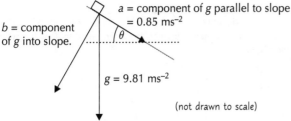

a = component of *g* parallel to slope
= 0.85 ms⁻²

b = component of *g* into slope.

g = 9.81 ms⁻²

(not drawn to scale)

Add angles to your diagram:

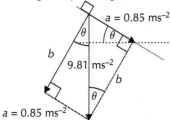

a = 0.85 ms⁻²

9.81 ms⁻²

a = 0.85 ms⁻²

sin *θ* = opposite ÷ hypotenuse, so:
θ = sin⁻¹ (opposite ÷ hypotenuse) = sin⁻¹ (0.85 ÷ 9.81) = 4.970...
= **5.0° (to 2 s.f.)**

Section Three — Graph Skills

Page 53 — Plotting and Reading Off Graphs

1 a)

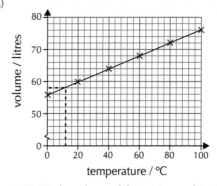

At 12 °C, the volume of the gas is equal to **58 litres**.

b)

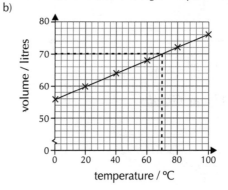

The volume of the gas is 70 litres at a temperature of about **70 °C**.

2

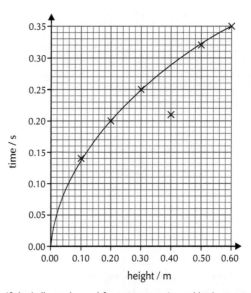

If the ball was dropped from O metres, it would take O seconds to fall, so the graph must go through the origin. The point for O.4O m looks anomalous, so ignore it when drawing the line of best fit.
The scales of your axes will depend on the size of your graph paper — your graph should take up a large part of the paper you are using.

Answers

Page 55 — Linear Graphs

1 a) The initial displacement is the y-intercept of the graph, so the runner's initial displacement is **4 m.**

    5 squares represent 10 m on the y-axis, so 1 square represents 10 ÷ 5 = 2 m. The y-intercept is 2 squares above 0 m, so the y-intercept is 2 × 2 m = 4 m.

 b) You need to calculate the gradient of the graph to find the velocity.
    E.g.

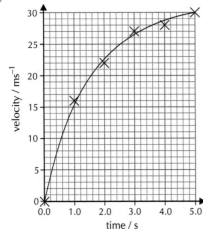

$$m = \frac{\Delta y}{\Delta x} = \frac{58 - 4}{9 - 0} = \frac{54}{9} = \textbf{6 ms}^{-1}$$

Page 57 — Non-Linear Graphs

1 a)

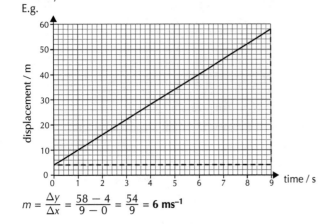

 b) Find the gradient of the line at t = 3.0 s:

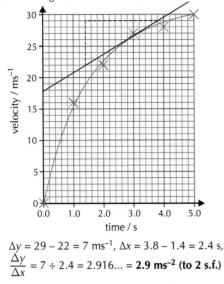

$\Delta y = 29 - 22 = 7$ ms^{-1}, $\Delta x = 3.8 - 1.4 = 2.4$ s,

$$\frac{\Delta y}{\Delta x} = 7 \div 2.4 = 2.916... = \textbf{2.9 ms}^{-2} \textbf{ (to 2 s.f.)}$$

Your line of best fit might be slightly different to the one drawn here, which means you could get answers that are slightly different to the ones given for parts b) and c) of this question. As long as your method and calculations are correct, you can mark your answer as correct.

c)

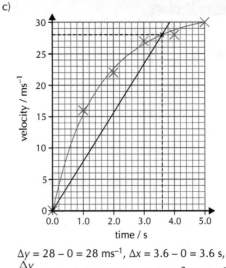

$\Delta y = 28 - 0 = 28$ ms^{-1}, $\Delta x = 3.6 - 0 = 3.6$ s,

$$\frac{\Delta y}{\Delta x} = 28 \div 3.6 = 7.77... = \textbf{7.8 ms}^{-2} \textbf{ (to 2 s.f.)}$$

Page 59 — Sketching Graphs

1 a) D
 b) B
 c) A
 d) C

2

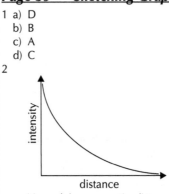

You can't have a negative distance, so you only need to draw this section of the graph.

3 a)

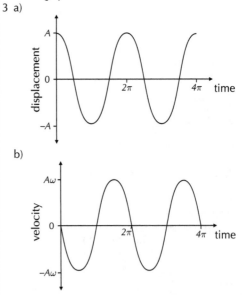

b)

You can't have a negative time, so these graphs don't continue to the left of the y-axis like the ones on page 58.
Remember, for b) you're sketching $v = -A\omega\sin(\omega t)$, and so this is a $y = k\sin(x)$ graph where the value of k is negative, so the graph is reflected in the x-axis.

Answers

Page 63 — Logarithmic Plots

1 By taking logs of both sides and using log rules,
$I = I_0 e^{-\mu x}$ can be written as $\ln I = \ln I_0 - \mu x$

x / m	0.005	0.010	0.015	0.020	0.025
I / Wm^{-2}	85.4	36.5	15.6	6.7	2.9
$\ln (I)$	4.447	3.597	2.747	1.90	1.06

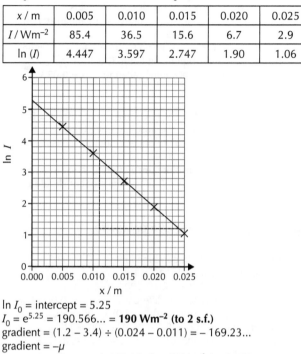

$\ln I_0$ = intercept = 5.25
$I_0 = e^{5.25} = 190.566... =$ **190 Wm^{-2} (to 2 s.f.)**
gradient = $(1.2 - 3.4) \div (0.024 - 0.011) = -169.23...$
gradient = $-\mu$
so $\mu = -$gradient = $-(-169.23...) =$ **170 m^{-1} (to 2 s.f.)**

2

volume / dB	intensity / Wm^{-2}	log (volume)	log (intensity)
15	3.2×10^{-11}	1.18	-10.49
30	1.0×10^{-9}	1.48	-9.00
45	3.2×10^{-8}	1.65	-7.49
60	1.0×10^{-6}	1.78	-6.00
75	3.2×10^{-5}	1.88	-4.49
90	1.0×10^{-3}	1.95	-3.00

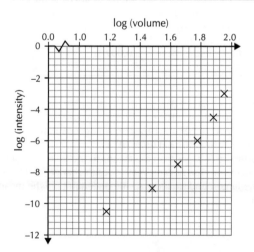

There is not a power law relationship between volume and intensity, because the graph of log (volume) against log (intensity) is not a straight line.

Page 67 — Rates of Change

1 $\dfrac{\Delta Q}{\Delta t} = -\dfrac{Q}{RC}$ so $\Delta Q = -\dfrac{Q}{RC}\Delta t$

t / s	ΔQ / C	Q / C
$t_0 = 0$		$Q_0 = 0.005$
$t_1 = t_0 + \Delta t$ $= 0.005$	$\Delta Q_1 = -(Q_0 \div RC) \times \Delta t$ $= -5 \times 10^{-5}$	$Q_1 = Q_0 + \Delta Q_1$ $= 4.95 \times 10^{-3}$
$t_2 = t_1 + \Delta t$ $= 0.010$	$\Delta Q_2 = -(Q_1 \div RC) \times \Delta t$ $= -4.95 \times 10^{-5}$	$Q_2 = Q_1 + \Delta Q_2$ $= 4.9005 \times 10^{-3}$
$t_3 = t_2 + \Delta t$ $= 0.015$	$\Delta Q_3 = -(Q_2 \div RC) \times \Delta t$ $= -4.9005 \times 10^{-5}$	$Q_3 = Q_2 + \Delta Q_3$ $= 4.851... \times 10^{-3}$
$t_4 = t_3 + \Delta t$ $= 0.020$	$\Delta Q_4 = -(Q_3 \div RC) \times \Delta t$ $= -4.851... \times 10^{-5}$	$Q_4 = Q_3 + \Delta Q_4$ $= 4.802... \times 10^{-3}$
$t_5 = t_4 + \Delta t$ $= 0.025$	$\Delta Q_5 = -(Q_4 \div RC) \times \Delta t$ $= -4.802... \times 10^{-5}$	$Q_5 = Q_4 + \Delta Q_5$ $= 4.754... \times 10^{-3}$
$t_6 = t_5 + \Delta t$ $= 0.030$	$\Delta Q_6 = -(Q_5 \div RC) \times \Delta t$ $= -4.754... \times 10^{-5}$	$Q_6 = Q_5 + \Delta Q_6$ $= 4.707... \times 10^{-3}$

So after 0.03 seconds, the charge on the capacitor has fallen to **4.7 × 10^{-3} C (to 2 s.f.)**

In this question, ΔQ is always negative, so when you add ΔQ to Q in the third column, Q gets smaller.

Page 71 — Areas Under Graphs

1 Split the area under the curve between 200 s and 500 s into smaller shapes.

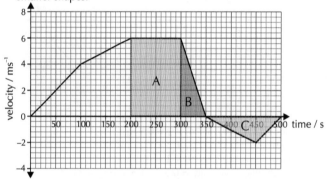

Area part A = $6 \times (300 - 200) = 600$ m
Area part B = $\frac{1}{2} \times (350 - 300) \times 6 = 150$ m
Area part C = $\frac{1}{2} \times (500 - 350) \times (-2) = -150$ m
Total displacement = $600 + 150 - 150 =$ **600 m**

Be careful, the area of the part labelled C is negative — it corresponds to Maya cycling back towards her starting position, so it decreases her displacement.

Answers

2   First, calculate the work represented by 1 square:
     1 gridline on the x-axis represents 0.0002 m.
     1 gridline on the y-axis represents 0.2 N.
     So each square represents 0.0002 × 0.2 = 0.00004 J
     All the squares with dots in them are fully under the curve:

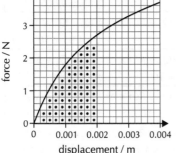

     There are 73 squares fully under the curve and a total area of
     approximately 8 squares from squares that are partially under the
     curve, so the work done by the spring as the trolley is displaced
     from 0 to 0.002 m is:
     0.00004 × (73 + 8) = 0.00324 = **0.003 J (to 1 s.f.)**

3 a) Divide the area under the curve between 6 s and 12 s into
     trapeziums. Three trapeziums, each 2 grid squares wide, looks
     good.

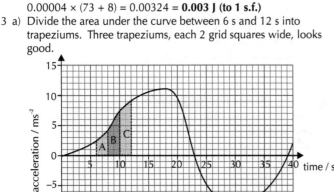

     area of A = ½ × (2.5 + 4) × 2 = 6.5 ms⁻¹
     area of B = ½ × (4 + 7.5) × 2 = 11.5 ms⁻¹
     area of C = ½ × (7.5 + 9) × 2 = 16.5 ms⁻¹
     total change in velocity = 6.5 + 11.5 + 16.5 = 34.5
                                = **30 ms⁻¹ (to 1 s.f.)**

  b) Because the line meets the x-axis in the area you're interested in,
     you'll need to break the area into triangles and trapeziums.

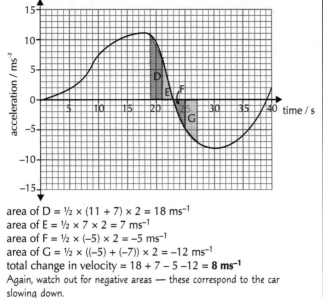

     area of D = ½ × (11 + 7) × 2 = 18 ms⁻¹
     area of E = ½ × 7 × 2 = 7 ms⁻¹
     area of F = ½ × (−5) × 2 = −5 ms⁻¹
     area of G = ½ × ((−5) + (−7)) × 2 = −12 ms⁻¹
     total change in velocity = 18 + 7 − 5 − 12 = **8 ms⁻¹**
     *Again, watch out for negative areas — these correspond to the car
     slowing down.*

Section Four — Handling Data

Page 73 — Uncertainties

1   The smallest increment the scales can detect is 0.01 g.
     0.01 ÷ 2 = 0.005, so the uncertainty in any measurement made
     using the scales is **± 0.005 g**.

2 a) The potential difference is given to three significant figures.
     One unit of the last significant figure is 0.1 V.
     0.1 ÷ 2 = 0.05 so the absolute uncertainty is **± 0.05 V**.
  b) 0.05 ÷ 10 = 0.005
     0.005 × 100 = **0.5%**

3   0.05 ÷ 25.0 = 0.002 so the fractional uncertainty is **± 0.002**.

4   5.0 × (2 ÷ 100) = 0.1 so the absolute uncertainty is **± 0.1 s**.

5   For ammeter A, the absolute uncertainty in a measurement
     of 1.2 A is: 1.2 × (2.5 ÷ 100) = 0.03 A.
     For ammeter B, the absolute uncertainty in a measurement
     of 1.2 A is 0.05 A. 0.03 < 0.05, so **the student should use
     ammeter A**.

Page 75 — Combining Uncertainties

1   365 + 152 = 517 g
     absolute uncertainty in combined mass = 0.5 + 0.5 = 1
     So the combined mass is **517 ± 1 g**

2   W = VIt = 10.0 × 2.0 × 25.0 = 500 J (to 2 s.f.)
     % uncertainty in potential difference = (0.5 ÷ 10.0) × 100 = 5%
     % uncertainty in current = (0.1 ÷ 2.0) × 100 = 5%
     % uncertainty in time = (0.5 ÷ 25.0) × 100 = 2%
     % uncertainty in work done = 5 + 5 + 2 = 12%
     So W = **500 J (to 2 s.f.) ± 12%**

3   kinetic energy = ½ × mass × velocity²
                    = ½ × 0.010 × 0.40² = 0.00080 J
     % uncertainty in mass = (0.001 ÷ 0.010) × 100 = 10%
     % uncertainty in velocity = (0.01 ÷ 0.40) × 100 = 2.5%
     % uncertainty in velocity² = 2 × 2.5 = 5%
     % uncertainty in kinetic energy = 10 + 5 = 15%
     absolute uncertainty in kinetic energy = 0.00080 × (15 ÷ 100)
                                             = 0.00012
     So the kinetic energy is **0.00080 ± 0.00012 J**

Page 77 — Calculating the Mean

1 a) (0.012 + 0.016 + 0.015) / 3 = 0.014333... = **0.014 Ω (to 2 s.f.)**
  b) largest resistance = 0.016 Ω
     smallest resistance = 0.012 Ω
     (0.016 − 0.012) ÷ 2 = 0.002
     So the uncertainty in the mean is **± 0.002 Ω**

2 a) $\dfrac{7.25 \times 10^3 + 7.19 \times 10^3 + 7.30 \times 10^3 + 7.25 \times 10^3 + 7.31 \times 10^3}{5}$
     = 7.26 × 10³ s
     largest half-life = 7.31 × 10³ s
     smallest half-life = 7.19 × 10³ s
     uncertainty = (7.31 × 10³ − 7.19 × 10³) ÷ 2 = 0.06 × 10³
     So the mean = **7.26 × 10³ ± 0.06 × 10³ s**
  b) The new estimate is larger than the mean, so including it would
     increase the mean. The new estimate doesn't change which half-
     lives are the largest and smallest, so the uncertainty in the mean is
     unchanged.

Answers

Page 79 — Drawing Error Bars

1   E.g.

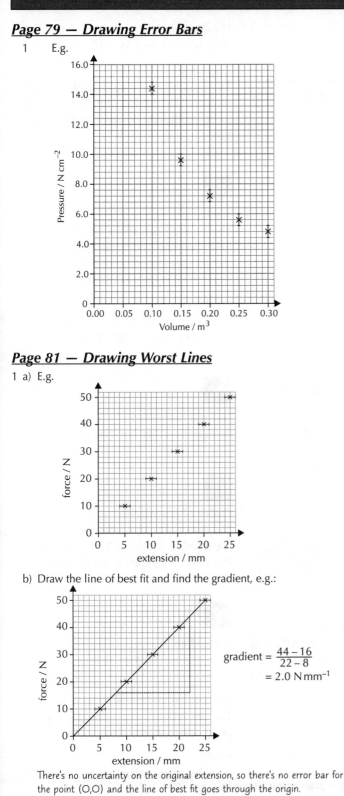

Page 81 — Drawing Worst Lines

1 a) E.g.

b) Draw the line of best fit and find the gradient, e.g.:

$$\text{gradient} = \frac{44 - 16}{22 - 8}$$
$$= 2.0 \text{ N mm}^{-1}$$

There's no uncertainty on the original extension, so there's no error bar for the point (O,O) and the line of best fit goes through the origin.

Draw the lines of worst fit and find their gradients, e.g.:

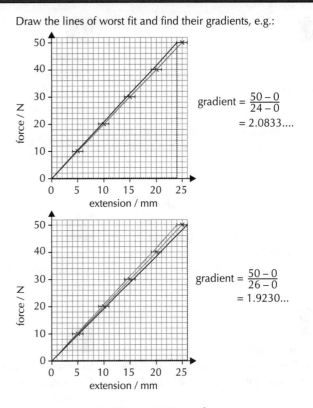

$$\text{gradient} = \frac{50 - 0}{24 - 0}$$
$$= 2.0833....$$

$$\text{gradient} = \frac{50 - 0}{26 - 0}$$
$$= 1.9230...$$

$2.0833... - 2.0 = 0.0833... \approx 0.1 \text{ N mm}^{-1}$
$2.0 - 1.9230... = 0.0769... \approx 0.1 \text{ N mm}^{-1}$
So the spring constant is **2.0 ± 0.1 N mm⁻¹**
The value of the spring constant calculated from the graph is only given to 1 d.p., so the uncertainty in the spring constant should also only be given to 1 d.p., as an uncertainty shouldn't be more exact than the value it relates to (see p.74).

Glossary

A

Absolute uncertainty
The uncertainty in a value given as a fixed quantity.

Anomalous result
A result that doesn't fit in with the pattern of the other results in a set of data.

Average rate of change
The rate of change of a variable averaged out between two points. For a curved graph, it is equal to the gradient of a straight line drawn between these two points.

C

Causal relationship
A relationship between two variables where changing one variable causes the other to change.

Correlation
A description of how one variable changes as the other changes.

D

Dependent variable
The variable that you measure in an experiment.

Direct proportion
Two variables are directly proportional to each other if increasing one of the variables by a certain factor causes the other variable to increase by the same factor.

E

Error bar
A line plotted on a graph to show the uncertainty on a data point.

Exponential relationship
A relationship where the rate of change of a quantity is proportional to the value of that quantity.

F

Fraction
A proportion written as one number over another. E.g. 1 out of 2 written as a fraction is $\frac{1}{2}$.

Fractional uncertainty
The uncertainty in a value given as a fraction of that value.

G

Gradient
A value that tells you how steep a graph is.

I

Independent variable
The variable that you change in an experiment.

Instantaneous rate of change
The rate of change of a variable at a specific point. For a curved graph, it's equal to the gradient of a tangent to the curve at that point.

Inverse function
The opposite of a function. Applying a function to a value then applying the inverse function to the answer returns the original value.

Inverse proportion
Two variables are inversely proportional to each other if increasing one variable by a certain factor causes the other value to decrease by the same factor.

L

Line of best fit
A line drawn on a scatter graph that fits the general pattern of the data and that passes as close to as many of the points as possible.

Linear graph
A linear graph has a straight line of best fit.

Log-linear graph
A graph with one linear axis and one logarithmic axis.

Log-log graph
A graph with two logarithmic axes.

Logarithm
The logarithm of a value is the number of times that the logarithm's base has to be multiplied by itself to give that value.

M

Mean
The average of a set of values, calculated by adding all the values in the set together, then dividing by the number of values in the set.

Model
A simplified picture or representation of a real physical situation.

N

Natural logarithm
A logarithm that is to the base e.

O

Order of magnitude
The order of magnitude of a number is the number to which 10 is raised when the value is written in standard form.

P

Percentage
A proportion written as an amount out of 100.

Percentage uncertainty
The uncertainty in a value given as a percentage of that value.

Prefix
A scaling factor that can be put in front of a unit.

Probability
How likely something is to happen.

Pythagoras' theorem
For a right-angled triangle, the square of the length of a triangle's longest side (hypotenuse) is equal to the sum of the squares of the lengths of the two smaller sides.

Glossary

R

Radian
A unit of measurement for angles. There are 2π radians in a complete circle.

Rate of change
A measure of how much one variable changes as another variable changes.

Ratio
A proportion written in the form $a : b$.

Resolving (a vector)
Splitting a vector into components that are at right-angles to each other.

Resultant (vector)
A single vector that has the same overall effect as two or more individual vectors combined.

S

Scalar
A quantity with a size but no direction.

Scatter graph
A graph on which data points for two variables are plotted, used to determine the relationship between the variables.

S.I. base unit
One of a set of standard units from which all other units can be derived.

S.I. derived unit
A unit that is made up of a combination of one or more S.I. base units.

Significant figure
A digit within a value that is expected to be correct (as opposed to a digit that you can't be sure about).

Standard form
A way of writing values using powers of 10. Values are written as a number between 1 and 10 multiplied by a power of 10.

T

Tangent (of a graph)
A straight line that just touches the curve at the point you're interested in. It has the same gradient as the curve at that point.

Trapezium
A 2D shape with 4 sides, two of which are parallel.

U

Uncertainty
An interval in which the true value of a measurement is likely to lie, often given with a level of confidence or probability that the true value lies in that interval.

V

Variable
A quantity in an experiment or investigation that can change or be changed.

Vector
A quantity with a size and a direction.

W

Worst line
A line of best fit which passes through all error bars on a graph, with either the maximum or minimum possible gradient for the data.

Y

y-intercept
The value where the line of best fit crosses the y-axis on a graph.

Index